Corrugating Defect/Remedy Manual

Sixth Edition

TAPPI PRESS
Technology Park/Atlanta
P.O. Box 105113
Atlanta, GA 30348–5113 U.S.A.
www.tappi.org

ISBN 0–89852–515–2
TP 0101R153

Printed in the United States of America

Foreword

We, as an industry, have come a long way from the original Defect and Remedy Manual that was published October 1, 1962. By 1988 the fifth revised edition of the manual was being reprinted in French, German, Italian, Swedish, Japanese and Spanish languages. The manual has come a long way during the past four decades and will celebrate its 37th birthday on October 1, 1999.

From its birth and delivery at the Twelfth Corrugated Conference in Boston by H. E. Dunholtman, Task Group Chairman (CA 762), our industry has seen vast improvements in the way corrugated board is produced. We now have pressure and vacuum singlefacers, computerized hot plates, non-type roller systems, beltless hot plates, direct drive knives and downstackers.

The industry has eliminated many problems during its growth and expansion. We are all aware of new changes and problems. The Sixth Edition touches on some of those new problems and reviews the old ones.

The Sixth edition was put together with the assistance of the CORBOTECH Sub-Bonding Committee along with many of the industry's prominent and experienced individuals, consultants, and suppliers to the corrugated industry. It is subdivided into four (4) parts: Corrugator Problems, Printing Problems, Diecutting Problems, and Finishing and Manufacturer's Joint Problems.

We have added Visual Glue Line Standards and we have improved on the Printing Problems section by using color photos in the CD-ROM version. We now cover the ink problems on Flexo Presses and a section on mechanically engraved ceramic-coated roll and laser-engraved printing rolls.

The manual will provide a basis for common knowledge of terms, definitions, and methods of correction of corrugated operational defects.

The dissemination of knowledge of this type should expedite the teaching of all personnel and permit a faster improvement in new techniques. However, it must be understood that the information given in this manual is only a starting point for the attainment of the objectives mentioned above. It must not be considered at this point to be a source of all the answers to corrugated container manufacturing problems. It is the nucleus for this source which we hope will be attained in the future.

It is therefore the hope of all who contributed to this publication that the attempts to define many of the common types of defects and their corresponding remedies with pictorial illustrations will not only be found useful at the present time, but will bring about a greater transfer of useful information in the future.

This manual provides standard definitions with photographs where possible. Several sheets have no illustrations, because it was felt that the defects were "self-explanatory." Lack of an illustrative photo is not an error—as we upgrade the manual, a new photo will be added.

Over the years, because individuals contributed their ideas, comments and suggestions, I have added an Honor Roll in order to recognize them.

The members of the sub-committee responsible for this TAPPI Committee Assignment No. CA 920304.10 are also listed as Contributors.

Contributors to the 1999 Edition

Chuck P. Harbit, Chairman, (1998-1999)	Bicknell & Fuller Paper Box Co.
Jody Brittain	J & J MidSouth Box Co.
David A. Carlson	Smurfit-Stone Container Corp.
James T. Carbone	Harper /Love Adhesives Corp.
Richard J. Croker	Georgia Pacific Corp.
John A. Curielli	Harper/Love Adhesives Corp.
Guy Desrochers	Mitchel Lincoln Ltd.
Craig E. Nordquist	American Packaging Systems
Cassie J. Corn Rothstrom	Enviro-Chem, Inc.
John H. Rutherford	Inland Paperboard and Packaging
Raymond R. Shultz	Beacon Container Corp.
Hal W. Tanner	International Paper
Frank Vincent	Georgia Pacific Corp.

In addition to the sub-committee members, the following TAPPI members have contributed their comments and suggestions:

Jay Aldrich	Smurfit-Stone Container Corporation
Peter Basler	Bobst
Stanley Field	Flint Ink
John Harrison	Ward Machinery
Kevin W. Koelsch	Dynamic Dies, Inc.
John J. Kubinsky	Harper Corp.
Ray Rammelsberg	Valco Cincinnati
C. F. Russell	Sun Chemical Corporation
Jack Simpson	Container Graphics Corporation
James M. Smithwick, Jr.	Container Graphics Corp.
Davide Friedmann	General Mills Corp.
Joe Trungale	Pamarco

In addition to the members mentioned above, I would like to thank Mary Lynn Miller and Bill Stafford of TAPPI staff for all their aid in the publication of this manual.

The manual remains a continuing project of the Process and Quality Control Committee. It will be revised, amended and supplementary sections added to include the latest developments occurring in the corrugated industry. Your comments and suggestions are earnestly requested and should be directed to the Chairman of the TAPPI Corrugated Containers Process and Quality Control Committee.

James T. Carbone
Harper/Love Adhesives Corp.
1999

Acknowledgement

TAPPI thanks Sun Chemical Corporation for their permission to use photos and text from the "Paper Packaging Troubleshooting Guide". This information appears in Part 2: Printing Problems courtesy of Sun Chemical Corporation.

Honor Roll

The individuals listed below were significant contributors to previous editions of this Manual. We honor them for their work.

H. E. Dunholter, Chairman (1960-1962)	Owens-Illinois Glass Company Forest Products Division
A. M. Schwartz Chairman (1963-1964) Vice Chairman (1960-1962)	Interstate Container Corp.
L. F. Ashwood	Downing Box Company
M. A. Burnston	TAPPI
C. Bassemir	Connelly Containers, Inc.
J. P. Corcorn	Packaging Corp. of America
S. L. Goodrich	General Box Company
J. W. Kirschbaum	Container Laboratories N.Y.
G. C. Lacky	St. Regis Paper Company
K. R. Martin	Olin Mathieson Chemical Corp.
H. G. Nelson	Owens-Illinois Glass Company
Paul F. Pratte	Georgia-Pacific Corp.
Manuel A. Rosa	Pro-Pack Testing Laboratory, Inc.
H. W. Seibel	Gaylord Container Corp., Division of Crown Zellerbach Corp.
Ned Varner	Union Bag-Camp Paper Corp.
David A. Carlson	Smurfit-Stone Container Corp.
Richard D. Croker	Georgia-Pacific Corp.

Table of Contents

Part 1: Corrugating Problems

A. Singlefacer and Doublebacker Defects
B. Fingerless Singlefacer Defects
C. Splicer Defects
D. Corrugating Roll Defects
E. Visual Glue Line References

A. Singlefacer and Doublebacker Defects

Blisters

Various shaped loose, unbonded areas in either liner. Liner appears to bulge irregularly away from flutes.

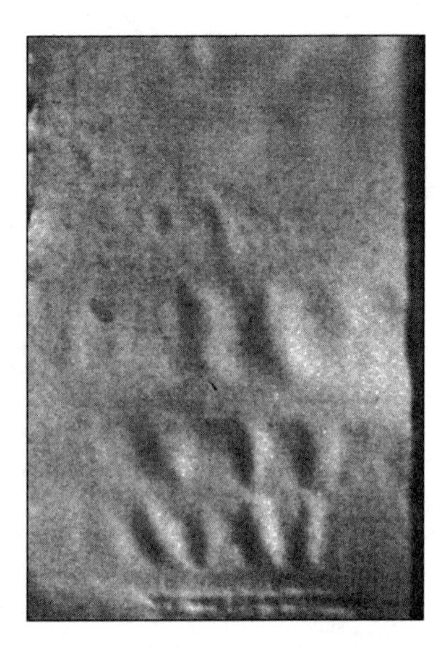

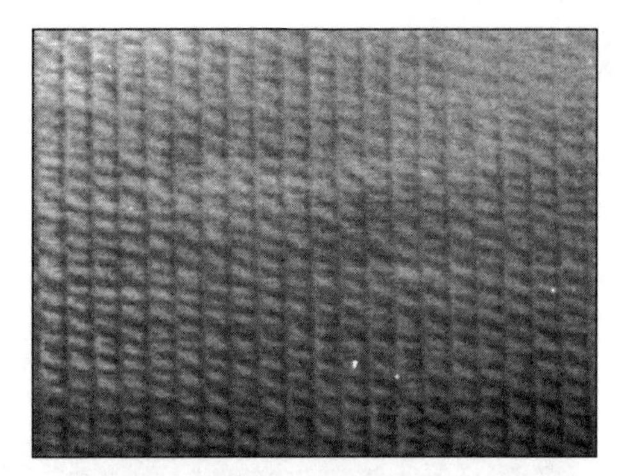

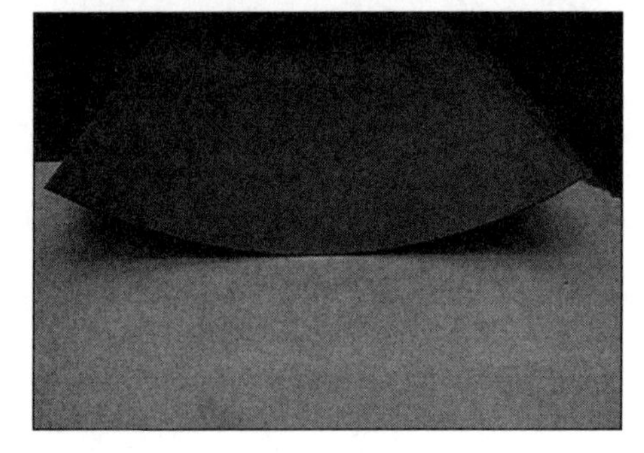

Blisters—while running

In center of singleface web, or across a substantial portion of the web (as opposed to edge problems) at high speed. May be continuous, but usually start as football shaped unbonded areas.

Condition 1

A soaked apart sheet shows adhesive was correctly applied to the medium and initial contact was made with the liner. (A good glue pattern was observed.)

Causes	Remedies
Lack of heat as evidenced by white glue lines.	Check steam pressure, siphons, steam quality for all pressure vessels.
Incorrect pressure roll crown.	Check crown to OEM specifications.
Wet streak in liner.	Increase heat to liner/medium by increasing wrap and/or tension.
Liner or medium tension not uniform across sheet.	Check for misaligned machine components. Check for improperly wound rolls. Use adjustable idler roll to ensure even tension.
Gel temperature of adhesive too high.	Check gel temperature and adjust to proper specifications.
Excess heat as evidenced by crystalline glue lines.	Reduce wrap on liner preheater and medium preconditioner.
Pressure roll not adjusted properly.	Back off pressure roll stops. Check pneumatic or hydraulic pressure roll actuating system for proper function.

Blisters

(Continued)

Blisters—while running

Condition 2

A smeared glue pattern on the medium (or spotty glue application at one or more fingers) caused by loss of control of the medium (fluffing out) on the lower corrugating roll before the lower corrugating roll/applicator roll nip.

Causes	**Remedies**
Mis-adjusted fingers.	Adjust fingers, both gap to lower corrugating roll and gap between finger tip and pressure roll.
Insufficient vacuum or cabinet pressure.	Increase vacuum or pressure.
Clogged vacuum holes or corrugating roll slots.	Clean holes or slots.
Dirty corrugating rolls.	Clean corrugating rolls.
Low corrugating roll nip pressure.	Increase nip pressure.
Worn corrugating roll bearings.	Replace bearings.
Low corrugating roll heat.	Check siphon pipes, steam traps.
Loss of pressure roll crown.	Replace pressure roll.

Condition 3

A smeared glue pattern on liner caused by medium fluffing out before pressure roll/lower corrugating roll nip. Same causes and remedies as Condition 2 plus item as follows:

Cause	**Remedy**
Applicator roll hitting flute tips.	Increase applicator to corrugator roll gap.

Blisters

(Continued)

Blisters—while running

Condition 4

No glue on liner.

Causes	Remedies
Glue roll/corrugating roll gap too wide.	Decrease gap.
Glue roll/meter roll gap too small.	Increase gap.
Steam shower condensate dripping on glue roll.	Fix shower condensate drain.
Cooling jacket leaking on glue roll.	Check by turning off water to cooling jacket to see if problem stops. Repair cooling jacket.
Gelled starch on splash apron wiping glue off medium.	Glean gelled starch off splash apron.
Starch level too low in glue pan.	Increase starch level.
Insufficient/no contact between lower corrugating roll and pressure roll.	Check pressure roll loading. Check pressure roll stops. Check pressure roll crown.
Incorrect pressure roll crown.	Check crown to OEM specifications.
Pressure roll not adjusted properly.	Back off pressure roll stops. Check pneumatic or hydraulic pressure roll actuating system for proper function.

Blisters

(Continued)

Blisters—while running

Condition 5

Blisters on singleface side of board.

Causes	Remedies
Thin streak in liner.	Add brake tension to increase liner contact with preheater. Wrap the portion of an idler roll in line with the blisters with liner to increase tension on liner and contact with preheater. Change liner.
Loose corrugations.	Check medium moisture.

Condition 6

Blisters on doubleback side of board.

Causes	Remedies
Not enough adhesive in some areas.	Adjust adhesive system.
Thin streak in corrugator belt.	Replace belt.
Wide gap between belts.	Close gap or use one piece belt.
Only happens with "small" flutes.	Reduce starch to minimum. Increase starch solids. Decrease heat to first hotplate section. Increase run speed.
Thin streak in liner.	Add brake tension to increase liner contact with preheater. Wrap the portion of an idler roll in line with the blisters with liner to increase tension on liner and contact with preheater. Change liner.

Blisters

(Continued)

Blisters—at startup

Blisters (football-shaped) caused by a temporary out-of-round condition on the lower corrugating roll and/or pressure roll after the singlefacer is stopped for a period of time. The blisters cease a short period of time after startup.

Causes	Remedies
Condensate collecting inside lower corrugating roll and/or pressure roll.	Check siphon pipes, steam traps. Check differential pressure between supply and return steam headers. Differential should be at least 5 PSI for proper operation.
Warp of the lower corrugating roll caused by vacuum systems where lower corrugating roll is not heated or where a vacuum chamber above the lower corrugating roll is employed to achieve vacuum.	Minimize stops. Consider adding the feature which disengages the upper and lower corrugating rolls and idles them during any stoppages. Retrofit heated lower corrugating roll, if possible. Consider breaking off the medium web and idling the singlefacer until even heat is achieved and then rethreading the medium for startup if this alternative is less costly than the waste generated by starting up with a cold lower corrugating roll.

Cockles

Appears as puckers in the liner between the flute tips (on either side).

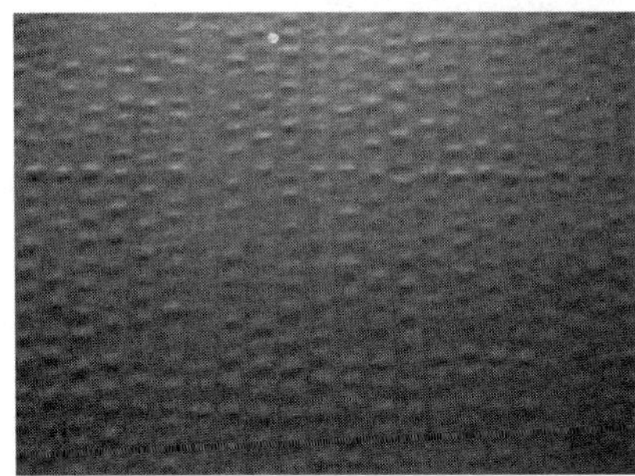

Causes

Adhesive application too heavy.

Too much heat.

Remedies

Lighten application.

To minimize puckers run as fast as possible (by passing preheaters) with the lightest practical gluelines.

Washboarding

Refers to the appearance of the singleface or doubleface liner which tends to follow formation (most prevalent in lightweight liners).

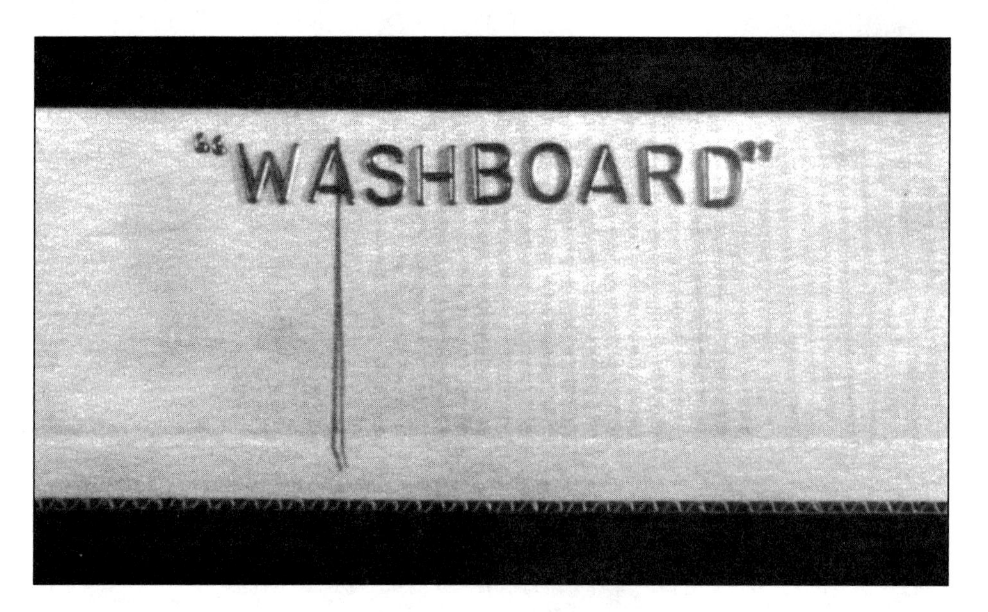

Causes	Remedies
Excessive adhesive application at SF or GM. Excessive TIR on metering roll and/or applicator roll. Metering roll gap out of parallel. Worn/damaged applicator and/or metering roll. Worn bearings on applicator and/or metering roll.	Inspect condition of applicator and metering roll. Check parallel of metering roll gap. Replace rolls if required.
Metering roll wiper blade worn or out of adjustment.	Inspect blade. Adjust or replace.
Too much rider roll nip pressure at the GM.	Decrease rider roll pressure.
Incorrect speed ratio between SFW and applicator roll.	Check speed ratio and adjust applicator roll speed if required.
Adhesive solids too low.	Increase solids in adhesive formula.
Adhesive viscosity too low.	Check adhesive viscosity. Adjust if required.
Worn corrugating rolls.	Inspect rolls and replace if necessary.
'High-Low' corrugations.	Eliminate 'High-Lows' rather than increase adhesive application. See High-Low section.
Liner moisture too high.	Adjust preheater wrap to remove excess moisture.
Too much heat.	Speed up, reduce temperature on hot plates, reduce preheater wrap on liners and SF web.

SF (Single facer), SFL (SF Liner), GM (Glue Machine), TIR (Total Indicated Run-out), SFW (single faced Web), DB (Doublebacker or Doubleback). Applicator roll (or glue roll), Metering roll (or wiper roll).

Corrugations—Loose

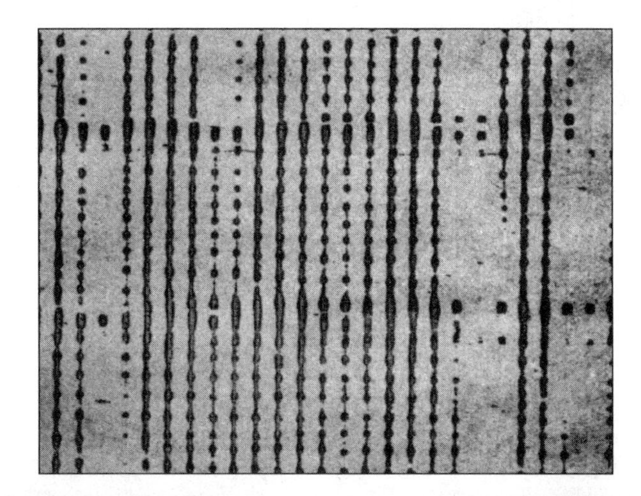

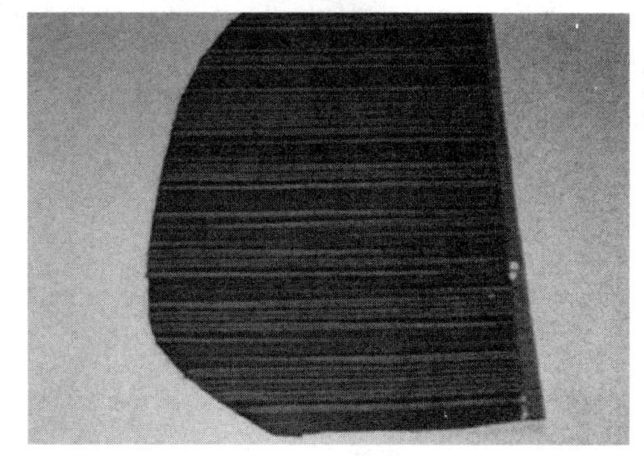

Condition 1

Fall-out—refers to intermittent groups of corrugations that have been distorted or pulled out of shape at the singlefacer and are not adhered to the singleface liner in contact with it. This condition can occur only at the singlefacer in the machine direction at any point along the line of corrugations being formed.

Causes	Remedies
Finger too low, fluttering medium in fluff out area of fingers.	Raise finger.
Broken or worn finger.	Replace finger.
Corrugating medium too wet or dry.	Adjust shower and wrap on preconditioner.
Uneven pressure on pressure roll.	Equalize pressure roll.
Dirty corrugating rolls.	Clean corrugating rolls.
Brake too loose on corrugating medium.	Tighten brake.
Uneven or not enough pressure on corrugating rolls.	Adjust or increase pressure.
Roll of medium out of round or loosely cored.	Adjust brake or remove roll.
Warped finger bar.	Straighten or replace bar.
Corrugator rolls not hot enough.	Check temperature.
Corrugator roll-glue transfer roll clearance too great.	Re-adjust setting.

Corrugations—Loose

Condition 2

Loose Liner—Medium and liner separating after initial bonding.

Refers to the delamination between the corrugated medium and the liner. This condition is often misdiagnosed as fluff out which occurs directly on the lower corrugating roll, whereas loose liner is evidenced at the incline conveyor.

Causes	**Remedies**
Clearance between lower corrugating roll and glue roll too large or too small.	Adjust gap and calibrate readout.
Clearance between glue roll and doctor roll too large or too small.	Adjust gap and calibrate readout.
Clearance between lower corrugating roll and pressure roll too large or too small.	Adjust gap and calibrate readout.
Low heat in corrugating rolls or pressure roll.	Check temperature, check traps, check siphons.
Low loading pressure on corrugating rolls or between lower corrugating roll and pressure roll.	Check loading pressure. Check accumulator charge. Check parallelism.
Medium too wet.	Check moisture, wet streak, increase preconditioned wrap.
Too much vacuum.	Reduce vacuum.
Adhesive gel temperature too high, viscosity too low.	Check adhesive condition.
Paper tension too high.	Check liner and medium brake tension. Adjust as necessary.
Pressure roll eccentrics too tight.	Need lubrication.
Singlefacer vibration.	Check bearings and bushings.
Liner slipping.	Check singlefacer acceleration ramp.
Medium too dry.	Check moisture, dry streak, decrease wrap, increase showers.
Elevator conveyor overspeed insufficient.	Check overspeed and correct. Check for worn or slipping belts.
Variable tension produced by elevator belt.	Check elevator belt lacing to determine if lacing is causing flutter as lacing pages over idler or drive rolls. Check sprocket and chain drive on elevator belt to determine if chain is periodically jumping a sprocket tooth.
Sudden acceleration of singlefacer that the elevator belt does not track fast enough.	Check acceleration speed of singlefacer vs. acceleration speed of elevator belt. Make sure there is no lag in acceleration of the elevator belt.

Corrugations—Loose

Condition 2

(Continued)

Causes	Remedies
Medium sticking in lower corrugating roll.	Check condition, adjustment of blanking plates/strippers. Consider use of epolene (wax) bar to assist in lubrication of medium. Check lower corrugating roll for cleanliness, roughness, or loss of chrome. Lower position of exit idler roll to assist flute release of singleface web from lower corrugating roll/pressure roll nip point.
Liner resisting adhesive.	Wrap liner to drive moisture toward glue line. Adjust speed to achieve a good bond. Try alternate supplier's liner to confirm problem. Investigate dry liner or high sized liner as possible causes. Adjust adhesive formula to assist in solving the problem.
Medium too dry or hard sized.	Adjust preconditioner shower and/or wrap. Try alternate supplier's medium to confirm problem. Adjust adhesive formula to assist in solving the problem.
Adhesive level in pan too low.	Check level, adjust to proper level.

Zipper Bonding

Post-corrugator observations that the singlefacer and/or doublefacer bond is weak, has insufficient pin adhesion, or has failed. Typically, the bond has appeared to be satisfactory at the corrugator at the time of manufacture. Because the observation is "post-corrugator", this condition is different than "Corrugations Loose", "Spotty Adhesion", or "Corrugations Loose Along Slit Edges". The causes are primarily paper-related.

No Photo Available

Causes	Remedies
Medium with a significantly higher float-curl (water drop) than normally run at the plant.	Reduce adhesive viscosity at the appropriate location (typically the singlefacer). Use alternate supplier's medium and discuss problem with the offending medium supplier.
Appearance of condition on high density liners (mills with wet end pressing capabilities) or on high performance liners.	Because "high density" and most "high performance" liners have more fiber per "point" (.001) of caliper, the heat transfer capabilities of these liners is higher than conventional liners. Increasing starch solids and reducing overall combining temperatures all along the corrugator have been found to correct this condition.

Singlefacer Liner Loose Along Slit Edge

Liner not bonded to corrugations along trimmed edge.

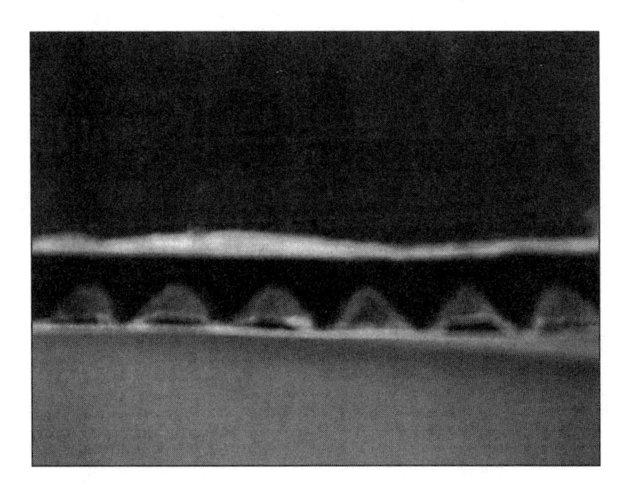

Causes	Remedies
Finger line occurring at slit edge.	Reposition web.
Guides too close.	Adjust guides.
Wet singleface liner.	Increase wrap on singleface preheater. If possible, move slitter knives.
Low caliper on edge of liner.	Increase pressure.
Not enough pressure on pressure roll.	Reducc overlap.
Too much overlap on knives.	Reduce overlap. Have knives sharpened.
Excess overspeed at slitter.	Reduce overspeed to manufacturer's specifications.
Dull knives with small amount of trim.	Slow down machine.
Pressure roll worn or out of parallel.	Replace or align pressure roll as required.
Foreign material on hot plate or doublebacker belt.	Clean belts and/or hot plates.
Running too fast.	Slow speed down.
Uneven wear of corrugating rolls caused by running various web widths.	Replace corrugating rolls or replate or regrind depending on the degree of wear.
Setting of pressure roll stops incorrect.	Readjust.
Glue deposits on pressure roll or lower corrugating roll.	Clean.
Uneven tension across paper web.	Make adjustment. Replace paper roll, reduce line speed. Increase brake tension.

Singlefacer Liner Loose Along Slit Edge

(Continued)

Causes	Remedies
Vacuum system not providing enough vacuum.	Increase vacuum.
Vacuum system—no vacuum.	Check system.
Wet or very cool edges on liner or medium.	Increase wrap on preheater or preconditioner. Reduce speed. Increase tension on wet edge using adjustable idler roll.
Dry edges on liner or medium.	Reduce wrap on preheater or preconditioner. Use all medium showers. Increase speed.
No glue at edges.	Adjust setting of glue dams.
Viscosity of adhesive too high or too low.	Change formulation.
Gel temperature incorrect.	Change formulation.
Gap settings incorrect.	Correct setting.
Glue applicator roll to lower corrugating roll or doctor roll to applicator roll.	
Variations in steam pressure (low temperature) on corrugating rolls or pressure roll.	Check steam system: traps, siphon pipes, drainage.
Elevator belt conveyor overspeed too great.	Check and adjust.
Preconditioner or preheater drum(s) too narrow or have concave edge(s).	Change preconditioner or preheater.
Excess adhesive at edge(s).	Check applicator roll ends for excess wear. Check for wear on pan dams. Check parallel at gaps between meter and applicator rolls or between applicator and lower corrugating roll.

Doublebacker Liner Loose Along Slit Edge

Liner not bonded to corrugations along trimmed edge.

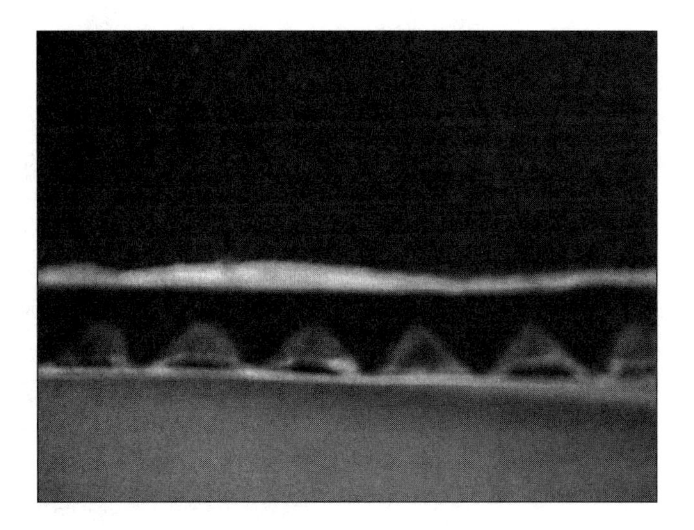

Causes	Remedies
Wet liner.	Increase preheater wrap.
Hot plates not at maximum temperature.	Check steam system.
Glue machine rider roll out of parallel.	Adjust.
Hot plates warped or out of level (knocks down flutes along edge).	Replace.
Belt lifter not down on one side.	Check mechanism, dirt under lifter.
Ballast roll lifted at one end.	Correct.
Dirt, adhesive or paper buildup or other foreign material on hot plates.	Scrape hot plates.
Knife pull rolls out of parallel.	Adjust counter balance.
Uneven (diagonal) tension on DOUBLEFACE liner.	Skew roll stand or idler roll.
Singleface web loose or wavy at edge on entering DOUBLEFACE.	Check machine alignment. Check bearings on liner preheaters and idler rolls.
Adhesive application not uniform—excessive or light at bad edge.	Adjust meter roll and meter roll wiper.
Glue machine crown breaker roll set too high.	Adjust.
Slitter knives dull or not set properly or loose on shaft(s).	Sharpen or adjust.
Operating too fast for conditions.	Reduce speed.
Too much overlap on knives.	Reduce overlap. Open clearance if score quality is not affected.
Worn edge on doublefacer belts.	Check belt caliper.

Doublebacker Liner Loose Along Slit Edge

(Continued)

Causes	Remedies
Insufficient edge trim.	Center slitter. Check for paper shrinkage. Reschedule with adequate trim.
Web weaving.	Check bridge web alignment mechanism. Check doublebacker liner for weave.
Hot plate top pressure mechanism applying insufficient pressure.	Check to see if the proper number or of ballast rolls are in good contact with the doublebacker belt. Check if the tapered ballast rolls are in the OEM specified sequence. Check to insure that alternate hot plate pressure mechanisms are functioning properly ("shoes", stationery belts, etc.).
Slitter shafts out of parallel, out of round, or have a bad bearing.	Parallel shafts or repair.
Incorrect slitter knife arrangement.	Set lower slitter blade bevel to outside edge on outside cuts.
Improper bevel on slitter knives.	Obtain slitter knives with proper bevel.
Improper slitter shaft overspread.	Set overspread to manufacturer's recommendations.

Spotty Adhesive Pattern on Singleface Side

Intermittent unbonded, bare spots in the singleface glue pattern adjacent to the fingers.

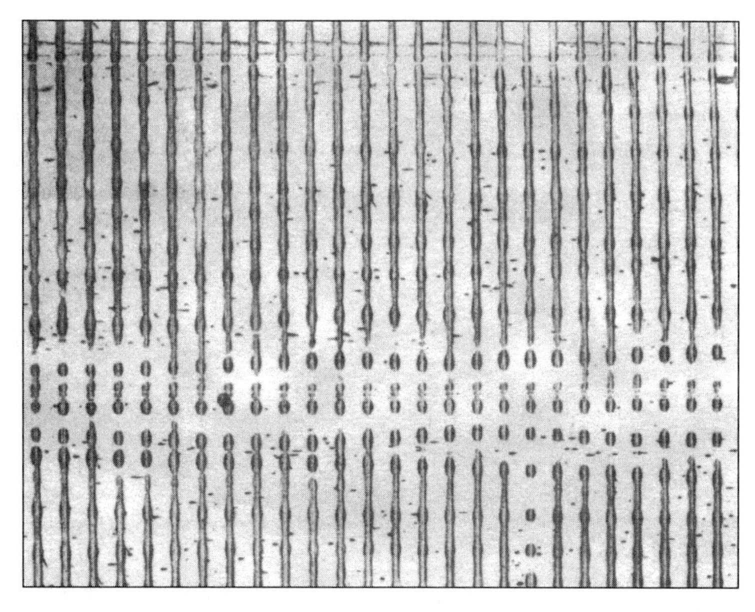

Causes	Remedies
Accumulation of gelled adhesive on fingers or in glue pan, wiping adhesive off transfer roll.	Clean fingers and glue pan regularly.
Finger too high or too low.	Adjust finger.
Wet medium.	Cut down steam on medium; increase wrap on preconditioner.
Adhesive too thick.	Reduce viscosity of adhesive.
Transfer roll out of adjustment.	Check clearance between glue roll and transfer roll and adjust.
Worn, bent or dirty finger.	Replace or clean finger.
Too much tension on medium.	Reduce tension.
Adhesive level in pan too low.	Check level.

Spotty Adhesive Application on Doublebacker Side

Intermittent unbonded spots in the adhesive pattern on doublebacker liner.

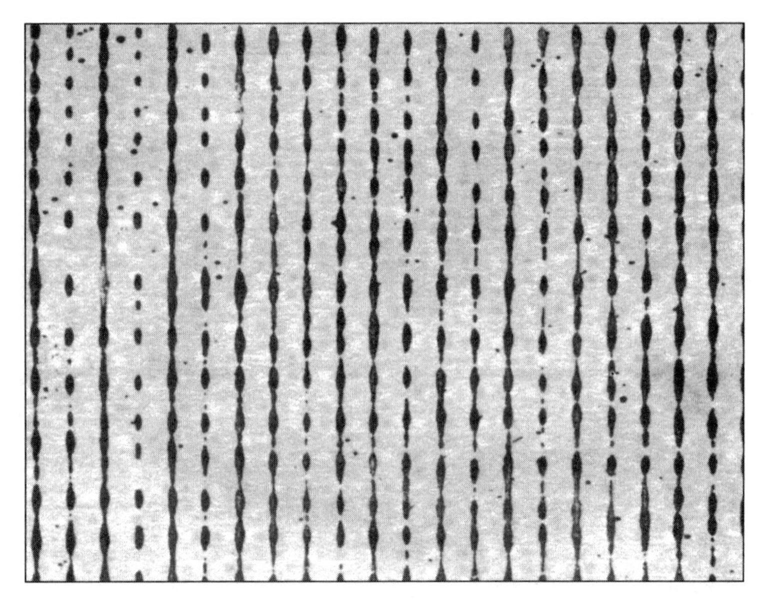

Causes	Remedies
Dirty glue doctor (or meter) roll.	Clean doctor (or meter) roll.
Variation of glue doctor roll setting across machine.	Adjust glue doctor roll equally on both sides of machine at proper setting.
Gelled adhesive in pan wiping adhesive off transfer roll.	Clean pan.
Glue machine rider roll set too high or too low.	Re-adjust setting.
Glue applicator roll dirty, pockets in engraving filled in some areas.	Clean roll.

Warped Board—Normal

Board does not lie flat. Warp is inward toward the singleface side.

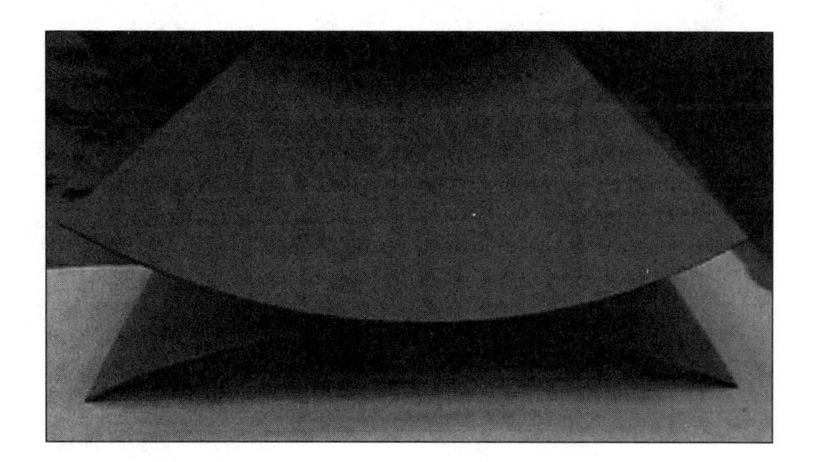

Causes	Remedies
Wet SFL liner.	Increase wrap on SFL preheater or slow down.
Combination of unbalanced liners.	Reduce heat on doublebacker plates and reduce adhesive application at singlefacer for unbalanced liners.
Too much heat on doublebacker.	Speed up corrugator (if possible) or reduce heat on doublebacker.
Excess moisture concentrated at the singleface side. This causes normal warp of board toward singleface side or upward from the hot plates.	Increase preheater wrap on singleface liner. Increase wrap on singleface board preheater (at end of bridge). Decrease hot plate temperature if possible. Use minimum amount of adhesive on singlefacer consistent with a good bond. Decrease wrap on double face liner preheater. Decrease the amount of festoons in the bridge. Exchange SFL roll for a "drier" roll. Exchange DFL roll for a "wetter" roll. Apply segmented shower to the doubleface liner.

NOTE: As long as the adhesive bond is adequate, it is not recommended to add adhesive to control warp as this practice causes other quality problems (post-corrugator warp and soft board) and increases cost.

Warped Board—Reverse

Board does not lie flat. Warp is inward toward doubleface side.

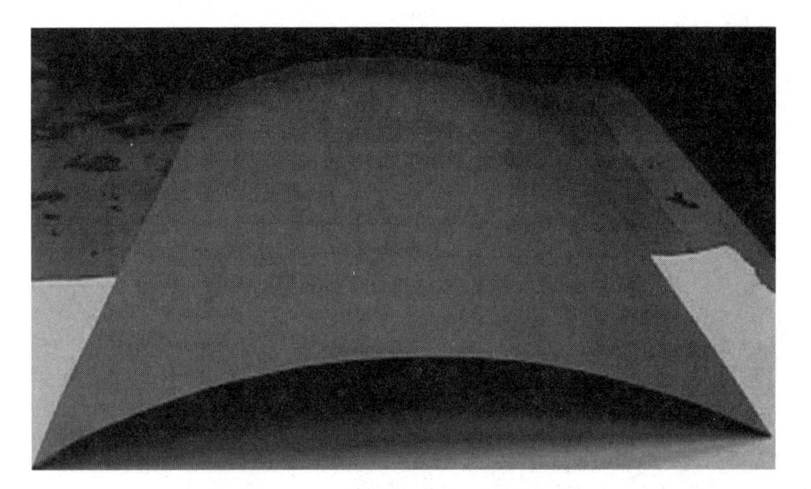

Causes	Remedies
Wet DFL liner.	Increase wrap on DFL preheater or slow down.
Combination of unbalanced liners.	Increase heat on doublebacker plates and reduce adhesive application at doublebacker for unbalanced liners.
Insufficient heat on doublebacker.	Make sure all ballast rollers are used. Make sure hot plates have maximum heat. As a last resort, decrease speed.
Excess moisture on doubleface side of board. This causes warp or curvature toward the doubleface liner or downward toward the hot plate.	Decrease preheater wrap on singleface liner. Decrease or eliminate preheater wrap on singleface board (at end of bridge). Increase preheater wrap on outside liner (DB). Decrease adhesive application at doublefacer consistent with good bond. Apply segmented water shower to singleface web. Decrease speed if practical (last resort). Increase hot plate temperature, if possible. Increase application of adhesive on singlefacer and decrease amount on doublebacker (last resort). Increase the amount of SFW on the bridge. Exchange DFL roll for a "drier" roll. Exchange SFL roll for a "wetter" roll.

NOTE: As long as the adhesive bond is adequate,it is not recommended to add adhesive to control warp as this practice causes other quality problems (post-corrugator warp and soft board) and increases cost.

SF (Single facer), SFL (SF Liner), GM (Glue Machine), TIR (Total Indicated Run-out), SFW (single faced Web), DB (Doublebacker or Doubleback). Applicator roll (or glue roll), Metering roll (or wiper roll).

Warped Board—"S"

Side-to-side warp that is both "normal" and "reverse" at different locations in the same sheet.

No Photo Available

Causes

Uneven adhesive application across the web at either the singlefacer or doublefacer.

Uneven contact with preheater at the singleface liner, singleface web, or doubleface liner position.

Wet or dry streaks in the singleface or doubleface liner.

Remedies

Check adhesive application at both the singlefacer and doublefacer and correct if any cross-direction variation is found.

Check for even contact between liner or web and appropriate preheater and correct, if possible.

Use segmented water spray at the singleface web or doubleface liner as appropriate.
If the segmented water spray use does not correct the problem, consider different roll(s) of liner or liner roll(s) from a different supplier (if available).

Warped Board—Machine Direction

Board does not lie flat in the machine direction. Can be either toward the singleface side (up) or the doubleface side (down). Frequently called "tension warp" or "end-to-end"warp.

No Photo Available

Causes (Tension Warp Up)	Remedies
Too much tension or drag on the singleface web.	Reduce wrap on singleface web as long as normal warp does not occur. Reduce drag on singleface web. Reduce brake on singleface web preheater.
Insufficient tension on the doubleface web.	Add brake to doubleface liner preheater. Increase wrap on doubleface liner preheater as long as normal warp does not occur.
Top and bottom doubleface belts traveling at different speeds.	Check belt speeds. Re-lag driving pulleys to achieve uniform speeds.

Causes (Tension Warp Down)	Remedies
Follow reverse procedures (causes and remedies) from those listed in the "Tension Warp Up" section above.	

Warped Board—Twist

Warp that exhibits characteristics of both side-to-side (normal or reverse warp) and tension warp.

No Photo Available

Causes	Remedies
A combination of side-to-side and tension warp.	Follow remedies for the appropriate combination of side-to-side and tension warp.
Idler arms out of parallel with machine.	Check all warp arms and idler arms for parallelism to machine and repair as necessary.
Corrugator machine components out of alignment, level or skew.	Check machine components for alignment, level, or skew and correct as necessary.
Split corrugator belts running at different speeds.	Check belts for speed differential and correct as necessary. Consider one piece belts.
Polar angler problems with liner(s).	Run one liner inside out to see if twist reverses. Try alternate liner supplier to see if problem disappears. Run two like-position rolls from the same mill at the singleface and doubleface liner positions. Consult with mill supplier for lab confirmation of problem and possible solutions including return of rolls to mill.

Flutes Formed Low

Corrugation height not up to standard. Flutes well formed but uniformly low, less than standard height (not to be confused with mashing of flattening of flute tips by glue machine rider roll).

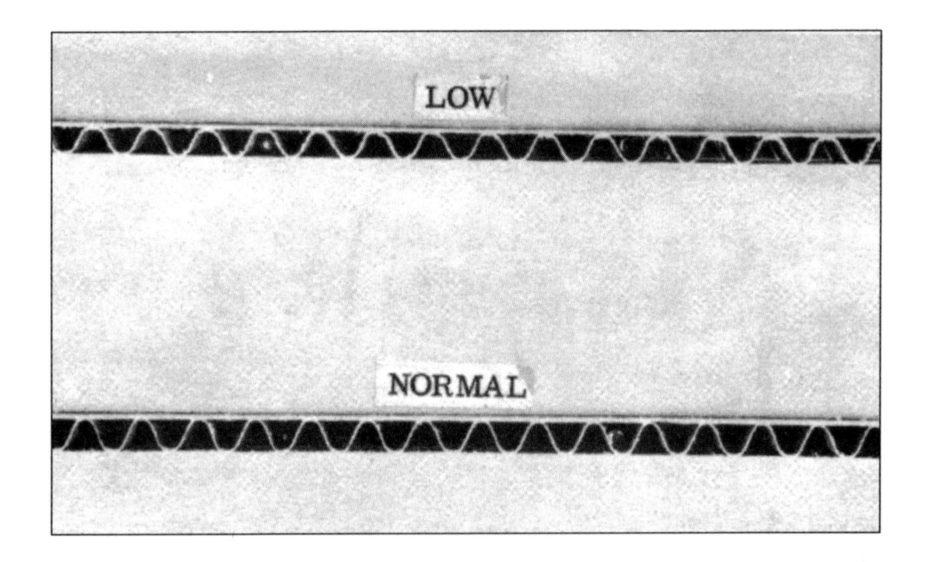

Causes	Remedies
Not enough pressure on corrugating rolls.	Increase corrugator roll pressure equally on both sides so that they mesh properly.
Worn corrugating rolls.	Replace rolls.
Corrugating medium too dry.	Increase steam showers at singlefacer and/or preconditioner.
Too much brake tension.	Reduce tension.
Wet medium.	Increase wrap on preconditioner and reduce steam showers at single facer and/or preconditioner.
Corrugator rolls are cold.	Increase steam pressure to yield a temperature of 350°F minimum.

Flute Formation, Caliper Loss, and Flat Crush

Flutes improperly formed low or initially formed low, caliper loss through the corrugator, and low flat crush.

No Photo Available

Causes	Remedies
Corrugating rolls out of parallel (leaning flutes).	Adjust parallel of corrugating rolls.
Initial flute height low or corrugator rolls worn.	Replace corrugating rolls.
Crushing of flutes after formation.	Check all nip points for potential crushing and adjust or repair as necessary: • Stacker or sheet delivery gates or spin off rolls • Cutoff knife pull rolls • Dry end coating or tear strip application nip points • Tachometer wheels that run knife cutoff control or overall corrugator speed control • Hot plates not level • Belt lifter mechanism not fully retracted • Dirty hot plates • Ballast roll(s) or alternate hot plate pressure mechanism out of parallel or not adjusted correctly • Nip points in older style web tension devices • Rider roll or bar at the doublefacer glue machine out of parallel or exerting too much pressure • Drag on singlefacer web in the bridge • Elevator belts

Flute Formation, Caliper Loss, and Flat Crush

(Continued)

Causes	Remedies
To much tension on medium roll.	Reduce roll stand brake. Check preconditioner for proper overspread. Adust, repair, or replace preconditioner driver motor.
Medium too wet from shower or adhesive application facilitating crush at any nip point.	Reduce medium shower. Reduce adhesive application at either or both the singlefacer or doublefacer as long as good bond is maintained and warp is not created. Medium roll initially has high moisture. Reduce or eliminate shower or replace roll of medium.
Doublefacer top and bottom belts not pulling evenly (leaning flutes).	Equalize speed of belts.
Low flat crush.	Check those factors causing crush (low caliper) after initial flute formation (see page 25). Check those factors causing leaning flutes (see page 27).
Medium with low Concora medium test (CMT) values.	Replace medium roll and discuss with supplying paper mill.

Corrugations—Leaning

Corrugations are leaning or tilted to one side, but otherwise well formed.

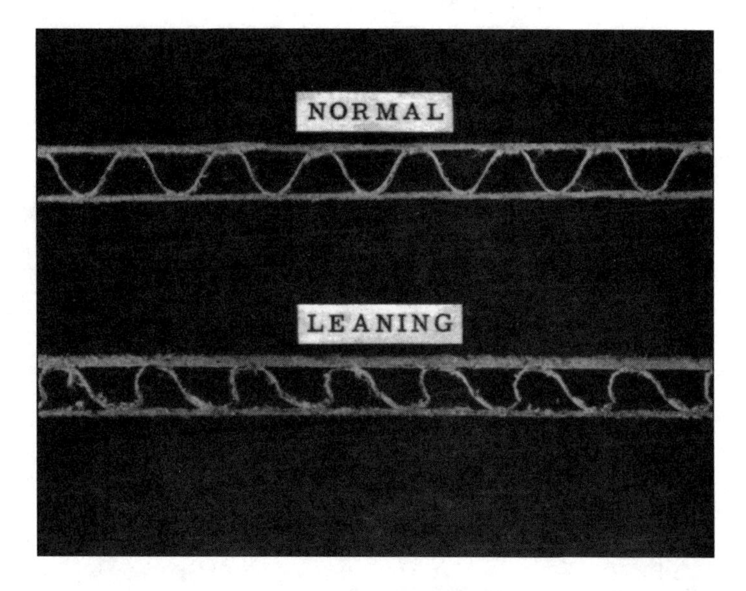

Causes	Remedies
Corrugating rolls out of parallel.	Adjust alignment of corrugating rolls.
Dragging of corrugations at some point between singleface and doublebacker.	Check travel of singleface to eliminate cause of drag.
Wet medium.	Reduce steam on medium: increase wrap on preconditioner.
Double-backer belts not pulling evenly.	Equalize speed of belts.
Rider roll at doublebacker glue station crushing the board.	Release rider roll pressure until it can be held back by hand pressure or gage adjustment with hydraulic unit.
Uneven pressure on corrugating rolls (true lean).	Equalize pressure.
Doublebacker hot plates dirty.	Clean plates.
Leading edge of hot plate extending above level.	Level edges.

Corrugations—Cut at Fingers

Perforations in the medium at the tips of the flutes in line with the fingers.

Causes	Remedies
Dirty fingers.	Clean fingers.
Finger too tight.	Lower finger.
Broken or bent finger.	Replace finger.
Burr on finger.	File down or change finger.
Dirty corrugating rolls (silicate).	Clean rolls.
Wet corrugating medium.	Adjust fingers for type medium being run; increase wrap on preconditioner.

Corrugations—Cut or Fractured

Corrugating medium which has been cut or fractured along sides or tips of flutes.

Causes	**Remedies**
Tension on medium too great.	Adjust brake. Ensure preconditioner is running at an overspeed to the medium. Preconditioner drum or chest is too cold. Increase to 280°F.
Medium too wet or dry.	Adjust shower and wrap on preconditioner.
Corrugating rolls too tight.	Reduce pressure on corrugating rolls.
Dirty or worn corrugating rolls.	Clean and check corrugating rolls.
Roll of medium out of round.	Slow corrugator or remove roll.
Corrugating rolls not parallel.	Adjust alignment of corrugating rolls.
Corrugating roll surface is too rough.	Check chrome for wear. If surface is other than chrome, rolls may need to be polished. Install a wax bar at medium station.

Dry Streaks at Fingers on Singlefacer Side

Condition 1

Unbonded bare streaks in singleface glue pattern running in the machine direction in line with the fingers.

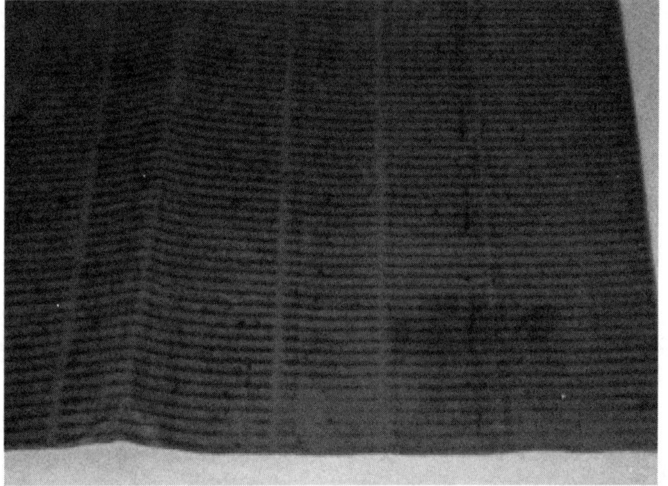

Causes	**Remedies**
Finger too tight.	Lower finger.
Adhesive too thick or too thin.	Check viscosity of adhesive.
Accumulation of adhesive on fingers.	Clean fingers.
Worn or bent finger.	Replace finger.
Finger not centered in groove of transfer roll.	Center finger.
Wide groove in transfer roll due to finger wear.	Replace transfer roll.
Tight edge on roll of medium.	Adjust position of roll.
Wet medium.	Adjust fingers for type of medium being run; increase wrap on preconditioner.
Finger slot clean-outs dirty or maladjusted.	Clean and/or adjust.

Dry Streaks at Fingers on Singlefacer Side

(*Continued*)

Condition 2

Slot lines–unbonded bare streaks in the singleface glue pattern.

These areas in both width and spacing correspond to the slot locations in the lower corrugator roll of a vacuum or pressure singlefacer.

Causes	**Remedies**
Too much vacuum or cabinet pressure.	Reduce vacuum or pressure.
Too much brake tension on medium.	Reduce brake tension on roll stand. Reduce tension adjustment on splicer. Too much wrap on preconditioner drum. Preconditioner drum not driven or not running at correct overspeed. Medium idler roll bearings bad. Spreader bar lowered into web too much.
Too little brake tension on medium.	Increase brake tension.
Wet medium.	Reduce shower, increase wrap on preheater.
Not enough adhesive.	Increase adhesive.
Medium roll out of round.	Reshape roll using roll truck clamps or remove roll.
Uneven roll web tension caused by out of parallel roll stand or roll stand clamp arms, or a tight edge on a roll.	Parallel machine elements or use an adjustable idler roll to achieve even web tension.

Dry Steaks at Fingers on Doublebacker Side

Unbonded streaks in the doublebacker glue pattern, in the machine direction and in line with fingers.

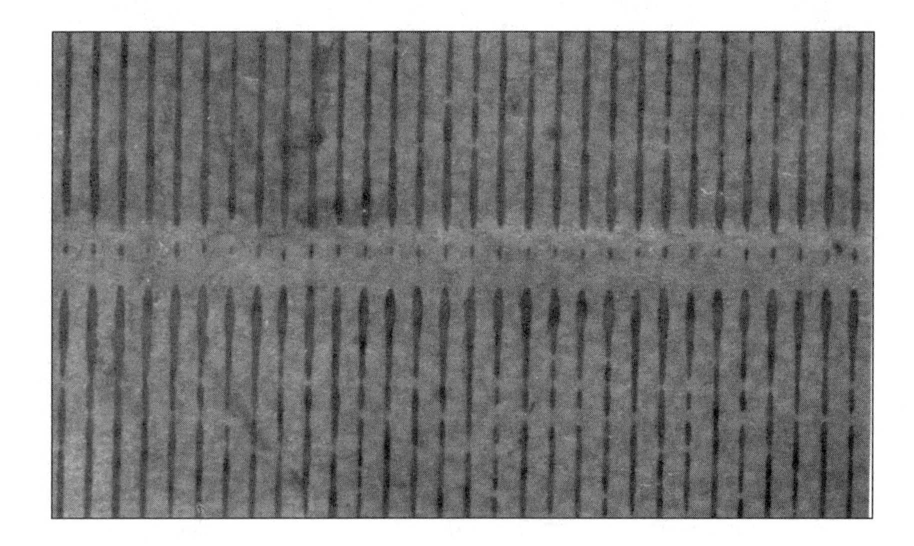

Causes	Remedies
Too much tension on medium causing it to sink into grooves in upper corrugating roll. This in turn leaves a low spot on the doublebacker side of the medium which does not pick up glue as it passes over the doublebacker transfer roll.	Reduce steam and loosen brake on medium.
Corrugating roll dirty.	Clean roll.
Wet medium.	Cut down steam shower on medium; increase wrap on preconditioner.
Wide grooves in corrugating roll due to finger wear.	Replace corrugating rolls.
Too much vacuum or cabinet pressure causes ridge in medium. Doublebacker side of medium does not pick up adhesive on each side of ridge.	Reduce vacuum or cabinet pressure.

Liner Damaged at Fingers

Bruised or perforated spots in the singleface liner occurring at the tips of the flutes and in line with the finger.

Cause

Bent or mis-adjusted finger riding on pressure roll.

Remedy

Adjust or replace finger.

Corrugations—High and Low

High-low corrugations shown by irregular glue pattern on doublebacker liner occur when corrugations are not formed uniformly in height.

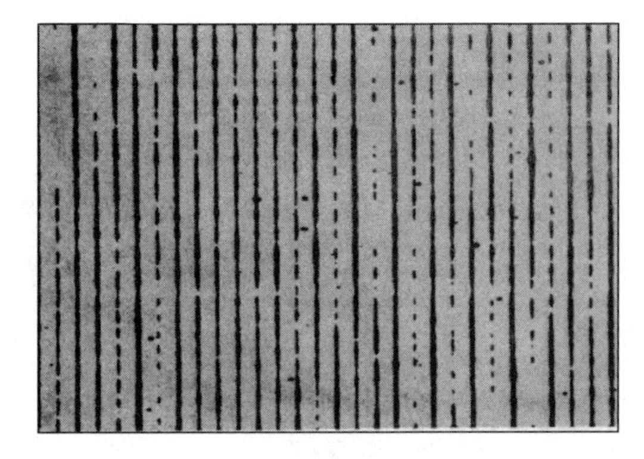

The most frequent causes of high-lows in singlefacers are the fingers and the release of the medium from the roll labyrinth. In fingerless machines, the most frequent and significant cause of this defect has been eliminated.

While high-low flute formations have been observed from fingerless singlefacers, the degree of the defect is considerably less than that found in fingered machines.

The following defect and cause analysis has been developed to provide guidance to the machine operator when high-lows are observed. While the singlefacer is the principal source of problems, other sources are included.

Causes	**Remedies**
A. Medium	
Medium too wet or too dry.	Adjust preconditioner wrap or steam shower. Change roll if necessary.
Medium roll out of round or wound loose.	Use medium tension roll if possible. Change roll if necessary.
Rough medium or other medium-related runnablility problems.	Try another roll from the same supplier and then a medium roll from an alternate supplier. If problems appear to be paper-related, seek assistance from the medium supplier's technical representative.
B. Corrugating Rolls	
Dirty corrugating rolls.	Clean corrugating rolls.
Worn bearings.	Check bearings. Replace if necessary.
Rolls damaged or rough.	Hone rough surface or replace rolls.
Vibration of corrugating rolls at critical speed.	Check corrugator roll adjustment. Run machine above or below critical speed.

Corrugations—High and Low

(Continued)

Causes	Remedies
C. Single Facer—Fingered	
Fingers worn, broken, or bent.	Replace fingers.
Fingers back too far.	Check and adjust fingers.
Air bag pressure low or air bag too hard.	Adjust pressure or replace air bag if required.
Accumulation of adhesive on finger.	Clean fingers.
D. Single Facer—Fingerless	
Insufficient vacuum or 'pressure chamber' pressure.	Consult manufacturer's manual for proper vacuum or pressure level. Adjust or repair as required.
Clogged vacuum holes.	Inspect. Clean if required.
Lack of smooth transfer of flutes to liner.	Check vacuum valve timing on machines employing a vacuum manifold at the ends of the lower corrugating roll. Check for proper fit (clearance) of vacuum blanking plates (strippers).
E. General	
Machine components out of level/alignment causing loose edge/uneven tension on medium.	Check level/alignment of roll stand, preconditioner, and singlefacer.
Preconditioner not driven or driven under speed or preconditioner drum locked (will not rotate).	Repair drive or adjust speed.
Preconditioning steam showers using 'dry' steam.	Re-pipe showers off return rather than off high pressure steam supply.
Uneven or too much brake tension on medium.	Adjust brakes.
Improper drag at bridge paper guide.	Adjust guide.
Doublebacker glue transfer roll out of round.	Rework roll or journals to eliminate the out of round condition.
Doublebacker glue transfer roll bearing worn.	Replace bearing.
Hold down roll or mechanism at doublebacker glue machine not parallel or out of adjustment with transfer roll.	Adjust for parallel.
Improper heat at singlefacer (usually too cold)	Check steam pressure, traps, and siphons as necessary. Bring corrugator rolls to correct temperature.
Incorrect loading pressure on corrugating rolls	Adjust pressure evenly on corrugating rolls — both sides.
Roll loading insufficient mechanism not working properly.	Hydraulic — check hydraulic system for leaks and accumulator charge. Pneumatic — check for air leak in bladder.

Score Cracking Or Cutting At Corrugator

Cutting or cracking of the scores at the corrugator by the slitter-scorer section of the corrugator or "light" corrugator scores causing a "rolling" or "wavering" score when folded.

No Photo
Available

Causes	Remedies
Improper alignment of male and female scoring heads.	Correct alignment.
Improper adjustment of scoring head clearance.	Increase or decrease scoring head clearance, as required.
Bent scoring shaft.	Check using dial indicator and repair if required.
Out-of-round scoring head.	Check for dirt or build-up on inside of scoring heads or shaft. Clean as required. Check that initial machining of corrugator scores was within manufacturer's specifications.
Mis-matched halves of scores on mounting heads.	Use only matched halves.
Scores on slitter heads worn.	Replace scoring heads.

Score Cracking or Checking at Flexo-Folder Gluers, Die Cutters, or Printing Presses

Liner split completely in segments or continuously on either the inside or outside liner (score cracking/rupture) or an incomplete split not all the way through the outside liner (checking). This problem appears most frequently on press scores running parallel to the flute direction.

Primary causes can be traced to linerboard, medium, low relatively humidity conditions, corrugator operation, or a piece of converting equipment.

Cause 1—Atmospheric (relative humidity)

Causes

Indoor relative humidity low. Corrugator board will condition to a very dry moisture content within 16 to 24 hours if placed in a low humidity (5–25% RH) environment. Low indoor humidity frequently occurs in northern areas when cold outside air is warmed up to normal working temperatures. Dry corrugated board will exhibit score cracking tendencies more readily than corrugated board stored in more normal (40%-60% RH) humidity conditions.

Remedies

Try to complete converting corrugated board into finished products within 8 hours after corrugating if your plant is experiencing low humidity conditions. Consider artificial humidification of your plant. This is an option that should be considered if low enough humidity conditions are persistent and of long duration and expected each year.

NOTE: Efforts to convert corrugator board before it dries to a low moisture content or to maintain plant humidity (see above) or attempts to operate the corrugator to retain moisture in the combined board just off the corrugator (see the following) may not solve the problem of score cracking, as many score cracking problems are paper related.

Cause 2—Corrugator Operating Conditions

Causes

Operating the corrugator to cause excess moisture removal.

Remedies

Wet End:

- Minimize singlefacer and doublefacer preheater wrap.
- Wrap preheater(s) to drive moisture toward the glue lines
- Maximize the use of preconditioner shower and Gaylord shower using saturated (wet) stream.

Hot Plates and General:

- Minimize the number of ballast rolls used or reduce the effect of alternate hot plate weight or pressure mechanism.
- Operate the corrugator at the fastest practical speed.

CAUTION: All corrugator operating adjustments to maintain moisture must be made with proper consideration of quality, particularly warp and loose liner.

NOTE: Since board off the corrugator will immediately begin to lose moisture if in-plant humidity is low, combined board should be processed within 8 hours after corrugating to minimize moisture loss.

Score Cracking or Checking at Flexo-Folder Gluers, Die Cutters, or Printing Presses

(Continued)

Cause 3—Paper-Related

Causes

Score cracking can be caused by high density paper making techniques and/or the increased use of recycled liners. High density liners allow less room to flex and bend at scores before exhibiting cracking or checking. Recycled fibers are typically shorter than virgin fibers and shorter fibers have a greater tendency to exhibit score cracking and checking when compared to liners made from virgin fiber.

Most linerboard consists or two (and sometimes additional) plys. Occasionally, under scoring pressure, ply separation can occur with the outside ply splitting causing a checking condition.

Occasionally heavy weight liners can be bulky enough to exhibit score checking or cracking when subjected to 180° bends in dry conditions.

Occasionally, board construction using 36# and 40# medium may cause score cracking if the medium is too rigid relative to the total board construction or scoring profile. This condition, when it occurs, is typically observed in rotary die cutter operations. While the condition is paper-related, the condition can be minimized by using a higher point scoring rule, adding additional crushing rubber adjacent to the score, using a surface mounted score with built up crushing material on either side of the score or changing the perforation spacing (e.g. going from 1/4 x 1/4 to 1/2 x 1/2 perforations).

Remedies

Some remedies are included in the discussion of causes 1 and 2 (page 36). Inasmuch as most score cracking is either humidity or paper related, permanent solutions are not easy. If a particular supplier's liner causes frequent score cracking or checking, (particularly if the problem persists during all seasons of the year), discussions should be held with the liner supplier's technical personnel. If the problem can not be corrected or minimized, alternate liner suppliers should be considered.

NOTE: Score checking or cracking as described in this section may be detected at the converting or finishing operations, but also may not appear until finished products are warehoused either at the box plant or at a customer's facility. For this reason, traceability of paper suppliers for individual rolls is important. Further, since moisture loss due to low humidity storage atmospheres continues, measures such as applying water or water with soap or glycerin, which temporarily appears to solve the problem, may, in reality, not do any real good. Cracking will reappear later.

Post-corrugator score cracking or checking caused by flexo-folder gluer, printing press, or die cutter operation is covered on page 152 of the Die Cutter section and page 176 of the Finishing section.

Slitting And/Or Cutoff Ragged

Ragged appearance of slit edge or cutoff end of sheet.

No Photo Available

Causes	Remedies
Cutoff knife not tuned correctly.	Tune cutoff knife to manufacturer's specifications.
Cutoff knife not timed properly with liner speed.	Time cutoff knife to line speed.
Bevel on slitter knives too shallow.	Replace slitter knives with knives that have proper bevel.
Slitter knives set too deep.	Open gap between upper and lower slitter shafts as long as scoring quality is not compromised. Replace slitter knives with those that will function properly with your corrugator scores.
Slitter knives improperly set.	Re-set slitter knives for proper contact. Rearrange slitter knives so that the two outside pairs of slitter knives have the upper and lower bevels set opposite from each other.

Facing and Medium Edges not Properly Aligned (Off Line)

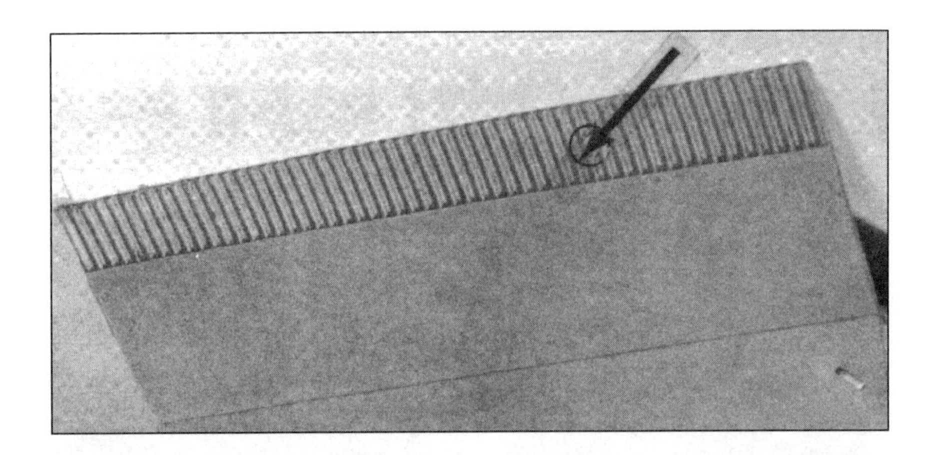

Causes	Remedies
Liner and medium not properly aligned on roll stands.	Reposition liner or medium on roll stands.
Telescoping roll stock.	Use a chuck with a wide flange attached to keep the stock in position. Adjust roll position as roll unwinds to compensate for telescoping.
Roll stand drifting.	Lock roll stand in position.
Under width roll or wrong roll used.	Replace roll.
Excess paper shrinkage.	Adjust operating conditions to minimize shrinkage. Replace roll.

Singleface Liner Damaged by Excessive Pressure (Pressure Roll Cutting)

Condition 1

Bruised and cut singlefacer liner along the line of contact with corrugations.

Causes	**Remedies**
Pressure roll too tight.	Release pressure on pressure roll to a point where proper adhesion is still obtained with minimum damage to liner.
Dirty pressure roll.	Scrape pressure roll.
Wet liner.	Increase wrap on singleface preheater.
Worn or out of round pressure roll.	Replace pressure roll.
Unevenly worn corrugating rolls.	Replace corrugating rolls.
Pressure roll out of parallel.	Check pressure roll alignment and make parallel.
Dense streak in liner.	Work through problem. Replace liner.

Singleface Liner Damaged by Excessive Pressure (Pressure Roll Cutting)

Condition 2

Bruised and cut singlefacer liner on the line of contact with the fluted medium but not limited to any certain position.

Causes	Remedies
Varying liner caliper or basis weight.	Check caliper of liner for excessive thickness variations. Hold up to light to check for uniform formation. Replace roll with roll that has a good caliper profile.
Wet streaks in liner.	Check roll with moisture meter. If excessive high moisture streaks are found, remove roll.
Inconsistent pressure roll loading.	Check for constant roll pressure—pneumatic or hydraulic. Inspect for leaks. Check hydraulic pump for proper operation. Check air supply for water and other contaminants. Repair as necessary. Check hydraulic accumulators for proper charge.
Worn bearings on pressure roll or lower corrugating roll.	Check for excessive bearing clearance while machine is hot. Replace as necessary.
Excessive runout on lower corrugating roll.	Check roll for excessive runout. Rework roll(s) or replace pressure roll as necessary.
Flat spots on lower corrugating or pressure roll.	Check roll surface condition. Rework roll(s) or replace as necessary.
Improper crown or loss of crown on pressure roll. Irregular diameter on lower corrugator roll.	Use pi-tape to check crown every 2 in. (51 mm). Compare to manufacturer's specifications. (Must be done while rolls are uniformly cold.)
Roll cleanliness, roll damage causing roll to run out of balance.	Inspect and clean roll(s) surface. Rework or replace roll(s).
Worn pivot pin linkage.	Inspect pivot pins and bushings. Replace as necessary.
Excess pressure roll loading.	Reduce loading. Make effective use of pressure roll stops rather than precisely trying to control loading. Check heat and adhesive as excess pressure roll pressure is often used to compensate for failures in these areas.

Wrinkles in Liners or Corrugating Medium

Creases or wrinkles in liner or corrugating medium.

Causes	Remedies
Liner wrinkled from mill.	Adjust tension or remove roll.
Tight or loose edges.	Adjust tension or remove roll. Check level/alignment of machine components, splicer and over roll.
Medium wrinkled from mill.	Adjust single facer spreader bar (older machines).
Uneven moisture (streaks) in roll stock.	Adjust preheater wrap.

Wet Board

Board combination excessively moist at discharge from conveyor.

Causes	Remedies
Insufficient heat in DB hot plates.	Increase heat or heat transfer in hot plates. Decrease speed.
Low steam vessel temperatures.	Check boiler pressure, steam traps, bypass valves.
Excessive adhesive application at SF or GM. Excessive TIR on metering roll and/or applicator roll. Metering roll gap out of parallel. Worn/damaged applicator and/or metering roll. Worn bearings on applicator and/or metering roll.	Inspect condition of applicator and metering roll. Check parallel of metering roll gap. Replace rolls if required. Reduce application after other corrective actions are completed.
Metering roll wiper blade worn or out of adjustment.	Inspect blade. Adjust or replace.
Too much rider roll nip pressure at the GM.	Decrease rider roll pressure.
Incorrect speed ratio between SFW and applicator roll.	Check speed ratio and adjust applicator roll speed if required.
Adhesive solids too low.	Increase solids in adhesive formula.
Adhesive viscosity too low or too high.	Check adhesive viscosity. Adjust if required.
Worn corrugating rolls.	Inspect rolls and replace if necessary.

SF (Single facer), SFL (SF Liner), GM (Glue Machine), TIR (Total Indicated Run-out), SFW (single faced Web), DB (Doublebacker or Doubleback).
Applicator roll (or glue roll), Metering roll (or wiper roll).

Wet Board

(Continued)

Causes	Remedies
'High-Low' corrugations.	Eliminate 'High-Lows' rather than increase adhesive application. See High-Low section.
Liner moisture too high.	Adjust preheater wrap to remove excess moisture.

SF (Single facer), SFL (SF Liner), GM (Glue Machine), TIR (Total Indicated Run-out), SFW (single faced Web), DB (Doublebacker or Doubleback). Applicator roll (or glue roll), Metering roll (or wiper roll).

Dimensions

Blank width, length, and/or score placement in error or varying.

No Photo
Available

Causes

Initial set-up wrong.

Unclear production card (factory order, master, etc.)

Scoring/slitting heads loose causing varying dimensions.

Cut off knife malfunctioning causing varying sheet lengths.

Remedies

Correct set up.

Seek clarification from plant office (customer service and/or scheduling).

Tighten or replace loose slitter and/or scoring heads.

If sheet length variation exceeds manufacturer's specifications, check the following:

1. Conventional knife
   - Control tachometer
   - Line shaft couplings
   - Knife electronics
   - P.I.V. belt
2. Electrical knife
   - Control tachometer
   - Knife electronics

B. Fingerless Singlefacer Defects

Defects Related to the use of Fingerless Singlefacers

Over the past few years, many fingerless singlefacers, either of the vacuum type or pressure type, have been purchased by the corrugated industry. Because fingerless corrugating is a relatively new technology, defects arising from the operation of these singlefacers were not included in previous editions of the Corrugating Defect Terminology Manual or its predecessor, the Fabrication Manual. These several pages will correct that deficiency.

Slot lines unbonded bare streaks in the singleface glue pattern

These areas in both width and spacing correspond to the slot locations in the lower corrugator roll of a vacuum or pressure singlefacer.

Causes	Remedies
a. Too much vacuum or pressure.	a. Reduce vacuum or pressure.
b. Too much brake tension on medium.	b. Reduce brake tension on roll stand. Reduce tension adjustment on splicer. Too much wrap on preconditioner drum. Preconditioner drum not driven or not running at correct overspeed. Medium idler roll bearings bad. Spreader bar lowered into web too much.
c. Too little brake tension on medium.	c. Increase brake tension.
d. Wet medium.	d. Reduce shower, increase wrap on preheater.
e. Not enough adhesive.	e. Increase adhesive.
f. Medium roll out of round.	f. Reshape roll using roll truck clamps or remove roll.
g. Uneven roll web tension caused by out of parallel roll stand or roll stand clamp arms or a tight edge on a roll.	g. Parallel machine elements or use an adjustable idler roll to achieve even web tension.

Defects Related to the use of Fingerless Singlefacers

(Continued)

High-low corrugations

High-low corrugations shown by irregular glue pattern on doublebacker liner occur when corrugations are not formed uniformly in height.

The most frequent causes of high-lows in singlefacers are the fingers and the release of the medium from the roll labyrinth. In fingerless machines, the most frequent and significant cause of this defect has been eliminated.

While high-low flute formations have been observed from fingerless singlefacers, the degree of defect is considerably less than found in the finger machine.

The following defect and cause analysis has been developed to provide guidance to the

Causes	**Remedies**
a. Vibration of corrugating rolls at CRITICAL speed.	a. Run machine below or above CRITICAL speed vibration band.
b. Dirty corrugating rolls.	b. Clean corrugating rolls.
c. Excessive medium web tension.	c. Reduce tension.
d. Corrugator roll loading pressure too low.	d. Increase roll pressure to recommended level.
e. Damaged or rough corrugating rolls.	e. Hone off rough surface or replace corrugating rolls.
f. Rough medium.	f. Increase shower. Use wax bar. Replace medium roll.
g. Wet or dry medium.	g. Use preconditioner wrap arm or shower to achieve proper moisture content.
h. Lack of smooth transfer of flutes to liner.	h. Check vacuum valve timing on machines employing a vacuum manifold at the ends of the lower corrugating roll. Check for proper fit (clearance) of vacuum blanking plates (strippers). Check position of exit idler roll.

Defects Related to the use of Fingerless Singlefacers

(Continued)

Pressure roll cutting—intermittent

Bruised and cut singleface liner on the line of contact with the fluted medium but not limited to any certain position.

Causes	Remedies
a. Varying liner caliper or basis weight.	a. Check caliper of liner for excessive thickness variations. Hold up to light to check for uniform formation. Replace roll with roll that has a good caliper profile.
b. Wet streaks in liner.	b. Check roll with moisture meter. If excessive high moisture streaks are found, remove roll.
c. Inconsistent pressure roll loading.	c. Check for constant roll pressure—pneumatic or hydraulic. Inspect for leaks. Check hydraulic pump for proper operation. Check air supply for water and other contaminants. Repair as necessary. Check hydraulic accumulators for proper charge.
d. Worn bearings on pressure roll or lower corrugating roll.	d. Check for excessive bearing clearance while machine is hot. Replace as necessary.
e. Excessive runout on lower corrugating roll or pressure roll.	e. Check roll for excessive runout. Rework roll(s) or replace pressure roll as necessary.
f. Flat spots on lower corrugating or pressure roll.	f. Check roll surface condition. Rework roll(s) or replace as necessary.
g. Improper crown or loss of crown on pressure roll. Irregular diameter on lower corrugator roll.	g. Use pi-tape to check crown every 2 in. (51 mm). Compare to manufacturer's specifications. (Must be done while rolls are uniformly cold.)
h. Roll cleanliness, roll damage causing roll to run out of balance.	h. Inspect and clean roll(s) surface. Rework or replace roll(s).
i. Worn pivot pin linkage.	i. Inspect pivot pins and bushings. Replace as necessary.
j. Excess pressure roll loading.	j. Reduce loading. Make effective use of pressure roll stops rather than precisely trying to control loading. Check heat and adhesive as excess pressure roll pressure is often used to compensate for failures in these areas.

Defects Related to the use of Fingerless Singlefacers

(Continued)

Singlefacer liner loose along web edge

Liner not bonded to corrugations along trimmed edge(s).

Causes	Remedies
a. Worn pressure roll.	a. Replace pressure roll.
b. Uneven wear of corrugating rolls caused by running various web widths.	b. Replace corrugating rolls or replate or regrind depending on the degree of wear.
c. Pressure roll out of alignment.	c. Realign.
d. Setting of pressure roll stops incorrect.	d. Readjust.
e. Loading force of pressure roll insufficient (hydraulic or pneumatic).	e. Increase pressure.
f. Glue deposits on pressure roll or lower corrugating roll.	f. Clean.
g. Uneven tension across paper web.	g. Make adjustment. Replace paper roll, reduce line speed. Increase brake tension.
h. Vacuum system not providing enough vacuum.	h. Increase vacuum.
i. Vacuum system—no vacuum.	i. Check system.
j. Wet or very cool edges on liner or medium.	j. Increase wrap on preheater or preconditioner. Reduce speed. Increase tension on wet edge using adjustable idler roll.
k. Dry edges on liner or medium.	k. Reduce wrap on preheater or preconditioner. Use all medium showers. Increase speed.
l. No glue at edges.	l. Adjust setting of glue dams.
m. Viscosity of adhesive too high or too low.	m. Change formulation.
n. Gel temperature incorrect.	n. Change formulation.
o. Gap settings incorrect. Glue applicator roll to lower corrugating roll or doctor roll to applicator roll.	o. Correct setting.
p. Variations in steam pressure (low temperature) on corrugating rolls or pressure roll.	p. Check steam system: traps, siphon pipes, drainage.
q. Elevator belt conveyor overspeed too great.	q. Check and adjust.
r. Preconditioner or preheater drum(s) too narrow or have concave edge(s).	r. Change preconditioner or preheater.
s. Excess adhesive at edge(s).	s. Check applicator roll ends for excess wear. Check for wear on pan dams. Check parallel at gaps between meter and applicator rolls or between applicator and lower corrugating roll.

Defects Related to the use of Fingerless Singlefacers

(Continued)

Loose liner medium and liner separating after initial bonding

Refers to the delamination between the corrugated medium and the liner. This condition is often misdiagnosed as fluff out which occurs directly on the lower corrugating roll, whereas loose liner is evidenced at the incline conveyor.

Causes	Remedies
a. Clearance between lower corrugating roll and glue roll too large or too small.	a. Adjust gap and calibrate readout.
b. Clearance between glue roll and doctor roll too large or too small.	b. Adjust gap and calibrate readout.
c. Clearance between lower corrugating roll and pressure roll too large or too small.	c. Adjust gap and calibrate readout.
d. Low heat in corrugating rolls or pressure roll.	d. Check temperature, check traps, check siphon.
e. Low loading pressure on corrugating rolls or between lower corrugating roll and pressure roll.	e. Check loading pressure. Check accumulator charge. Check parallelism.
f. Medium too wet.	f. Check moisture, wet streak, increase preconditioner wrap.
g. Too much vacuum.	g. Reduce vacuum.
h. Adhesive gel temperature too high, viscosity too low.	h. Check adhesive condition.
i. Paper tension too high.	i. Check liner and medium brake tension. Adjust as necessary.
j. Pressure roll eccentrics too tight.	j. Need lubrication.
k. Singlefacer vibration.	k. Check bearings and bushings.
l. Liner slipping.	l. Check singlefacer acceleration ramp.
m. Medium too dry.	m. Check moisture, dry streak, decrease wrap, increase showers.
n. Elevator conveyor overspeed insufficient.	n. Check overspeed and correct. Check for worn or slipping belts.
o. Variable tension produced by elevator belt.	o. Check elevator belt lacing to determine if lacing is causing flutter as lacing passes over idler or drive rolls. Check sprocket and chain drive on elevator belt to determine if chain is periodically jumping a sprocket tooth.
p. Sudden acceleration of singlefacer that the elevator belt does not track fast enough.	p. Check acceleration speed of singlefacer vs. acceleration speed of elevator belt. Make sure there is no lag in acceleration of the elevator belt.

Defects Related to the use of Fingerless Singlefacers

(Continued)

Loose liner medium and liner separating after initial bonding

Causes	Remedies
q. Medium sticking in lower corrugating roll.	q. Check condition, adjustment of blanking plates/strippers. Consider use of epolene (wax) bar to assist in lubrication of medium. Check lower corrugating roll for cleanliness, roughness, or loss of chrome. Lower position of exit idler roll to assist flute release of singleface web from lower corrugating roll/pressure roll nip point.

Blisters—while running

In center of singleface web or across a substantial portion of the web (as opposed to edge problems) at high speed. May be continuous, but usually start as periodic football-shaped unbonded areas.

Condition 1

A soaked apart sheet shows adhesive was correctly applied to the medium and initial contact was made with the liner (a good glue pattern observed).

Causes	Remedies
a. Lack of heat as evidenced by white glue lines.	a. Check steam pressure, siphons, steam quality for all pressure vessels.
b. Incorrect pressure roll crown.	b. Check if crown is to manufacturer's specifications.
c. Wet streak in liner, medium.	c. Increase heat to liner/medium by increasing wraps and/or tension.
d. Liner or medium tension not uniform across sheet.	d. Check for improperly wound rolls, misaligned external machine elements. Use adjustable idler roll to ensure even tension.
e. Gel temperature of adhesive too high.	e. Check gel temperature and adjust to proper specifications.
f. Excess heat as evidenced by crystalline glue lines.	f. Reduce wrap on liner preheater and medium preconditioner. Add shower steam.
g. Pressure roll not adjusted properly.	g. Back off pressure roll stops. Check pneumatic or hydraulic pressure roll actuating system for proper functioning.

Defects Related to the use of Fingerless Singlefacers

(Continued)

Blisters—while running

Condition 2

A smeared glue pattern on the medium caused by loss of control of the medium (fluffing out) on the lower corrugating roll before the lower corrugating roll/applicator roll nip.

Causes	Remedies
a. Insufficient vacuum or pressure.	a. Increase vacuum or pressure.
b. Clogged vacuum holes.	b. Clean holes.
c. Dirty corrugating rolls.	c. Clean rolls.
d. Low corrugating roll nip pressure.	d. Increase nip pressure.
e. Worn corrugating roll bearings.	e. Replace bearings.
f. Low corrugating roll heat.	f. Check siphon pipes.

Condition 3

A smeared glue pattern on the liner caused by medium fluffing before pressure roll/lower corrugating roll nip. Same causes and remedies as Condition 2 plus item "g" as follows:

Cause	Remedy
a. Applicator roll hitting flute tips.	a. Increase gap.

Condition 4

No glue on liner.

Causes	Remedies
a. Glue roll/corrugating roll gap too wide.	a. Decrease gap.
b. Glue roll/meter roll gap too small.	b. Increase gap.
c. Steam shower condensate dripping on glue roll.	c. Fix shower condensate drain.
d. Gelled starch on splash apron wiping glue off medium.	d. Clean gelled starch off splash apron.
e. Starch level too low in glue pan.	e. Increase starch level.
f. Insufficient/no contact between lower corrugating roll and pressure roll.	f. Check pressure roll loading. Check pressure roll stops. Check pressure roll crown. (See Condition 1: b and g.)

Defects Related to the use of Fingerless Singlefacers

(Continued)

Blisters—At Startup

Blisters (football-shaped) caused by a temporary out-of-round condition on the lower corrugating roll and/or pressure roll after the singlefacer is stopped for a period of time. The blisters cease a short period of time after startup.

Causes

a. Condensate collecting inside lower corrugator roll and/or pressure roll.

b. Warp of the lower corrugating roll caused by vacuum systems where lower corrugator roll is not heated or where a vacuum chamber above the lower corrugating roll is employed to achieve the vacuum.

Remedies

a. Check appropriate siphon pipes. Check differential pressure between supply and return headers. Differential should be at least 5 psi for proper operation.

b. Minimize stops. Consider adding the feature which disengages the upper and lower corrugating rolls and idles them during any stoppages. Retrofit heated lower corrugating roll, if possible. Consider breaking off the medium web and idling the singlefacer until even heat is achieved and then rethreading the medium for startup if this alternative is less costly than the waste generated by starting up with a cold lower corrugating roll.

C. Splicer Defects

Observation	Cause	Corrective Action
Condition 1		
Paper wrinkles/ tension warp	Worn brake shoes Slipping brakes Web tension	Make necessary brake adjustment or repair.
	Elephant-skin paper with significant caliper variations	Web tension is too high. Trim off the outer layers to eliminate bad paper.
	Festoon roll misalignment	Align all festoon rolls and the carriage assembly.
	Carriage misalignment	Parallel the roll stand chuck arms.
	Roll stand and paper roll	Check the roll stand arms for proper level and alignment to the splicer.
	Preheater/preheater idler rolls	Align preheater and preheater's wrap/fixed idler rolls.
Condition 2		
Paper web slack on one side	Roll stand and paper roll	Check the roll stand arms for proper level and alignment to the splicer.
	Paper preparation	Check that the roll of paper is wound evenly and not telescoped. Check for correct paper preparation. Adjust for uneven tension across prepared web. When preparing an out-of-round roll, a tight edge may be seen even though the splice preparation has been done correctly. Pull up the loose edge by approximately 1/8 inch (6 mm) and hold in place. Prepare paper for splicing.
Condition 3		
Missed splices	Failure to remove damaged outer layers on edge tears	Trim off any damaged outer roll layers. Trim out all edge tears, nicks using moon-shaped cuts as trained.
	Failure to remove a tight edge	See above procedure for slack web removal. Shift the paper edge in the head to align the web to the paper roll. Pull the web tight and press the clamp button to activate the paper stop bar. The web is now securely anchored and properly aligned to the preparation bar.
	Improper paper slack on the new roll	Each manufacturer will recommend how much slack (if any) can be left in the new roll before the splicer is actuated. Either too little or too much slack will reduce the chances of a successful splice.

C. Splicer Defects

(continued)

Observation	Cause	Corrective Action
Condition 3		
Missed splices	Improper paper slack on the new roll	Brake not set properly during pager preparation—set as directed in splice preparation procedure.
	Out-of-parallel nip roll not sealing the tape all the way across the web	Parallel both nip rolls.
	Cut-off knife failing to cut all the way across the web	Position the knife and anvil clearance as specified by manufacturer.
		Check the condition of the knife blade, anvil pad, and a mechanical bind-up.
		Ensure sufficient air pressure on the clamp bar and knife.
	Sluggish dancer roll or carriage movement	Check for a bind-up caused by paper dust buildup on the dancer roll or the carriage gear/rack assembly.
		Check for excessive tooth wear on the tips of the gear itself.
	Splicing at too high of a run speed	Each type of splicer will have an optimum splicing range depending on its design, type and condition of the material being spliced, condition of the roll stand, and the care taken in splice preparation.
		Recommend that the singlefacers and the doublebackers be equipped with easily seen speed indicators so that the operators will be able to make all splices at the correct speeds.
	New roll not lifted off of floor	Raise roll off the floor prior to splice.
	Machine operating out of sequence	Reinitiate manufacturer's recommended sequence.
	Roll of paper damaged in the center or edge; caused the damaged flap of paper to catch on parts of the splicer mechanism (more of a problem on medium due to its brittle nature)	Open leading edge roll damage should be stripped; management should find and correct the cause of the damage.
		Trailing edge roll damage should not be stripped because strip waste is extremely expensive.

C. Splicer Defects

(continued)

Observation	Cause	Corrective Action
Condition 4		
Missed "end-of roll" splicing at roll core	The tape securing the paper to the core can be stronger than the shear strength of the web; the splicer does not actuate before the web reaches the taped tail, causing the paper to tear out ahead of the splicer	Recommend off-the-core splicing be done with the roll; it is a risky practice on medium and low-grade papers.
Condition 5		
No brake	Control power off	Turn on roll stand power.
	Brake release light on	Reset brake actuation system.
	Brakes disconnected	Check brake system for integrity.
	Chucks slipping	Check chucks for proper position and clogged adjustable chucks.
	Brakes on manual control	Check brake selector position.
	Worn brakes	Check the condition of the brake pads.
	Highly sized and calendered heavy weight liners (slick surface prevents the splicing tape from achieving a good bond)	Take the leading edge of the new roll liner and "crinkle" it by repeated folding and rubbing the fibers to break up the slickness and soften the surface of the web. The raised fibers will cling to the splicing tape, thus improving splice reliability. If you believe the tape used is not aggressive enough, use a double width of 2 inches wide splicing tape to make a 4 inch wide splicing joint, thus increasing the strength of the bond between the two liners.
	Below-standard batch of splicing tape	Check the aggressiveness/quality of the tape by placing some of the tape on the liner, iron it down by hand, and then a new batch of tape should be tested.
Condition 6		
Splice failure	Low splicing-tape shear strength caused by stress during the splicing sequence or heat-related failure from the preheater or pre-conditioner; preconditioner not driven	Remove the wrap arms on preheaters just before splice actuation. Do not slow down the corrugator excessively as the splice passes over these heated vessels. Do not apply excessive brake on the new web before the spliced joint passes over these units.

C. Splicer Defects

(continued)

Observation	Cause	Corrective Action
Condition 7		
Tear outs	Improper paper line up causing tear outs	Care must be taken to line up the new roll with the running web before the splice preparation is completed. Once the leading edge of the new web is inserted in the splicer, any side-wise movement of the roll stand can induce a diagonal stress in the new web and cause a tear out when the splice is actuated. This factor is especially critical on medium splices. Preconditioner must be run at an overspeed to help prefeed the medium and thus reduce tension.
		Apply adhesive transfer tape to the bottom edge of the preparation bar. Cut the paper flush across bottom edge of the paper bar and trim the corners back at a 45° angle.
	Applying tape too high or unevenly across the web	Apply the tape flush across the bottom edge of the preparation bar or as directed by equipment manufacturer. Placement is sometimes critical to the splice reliability as the positioning of the tape interfaces with the splice head mechanism.
	Improper utilization of the splicer index system or failure to index web will result in an incorrect placement of the prepared web	Index the web as required by the manufacturer.
	Failure to remove tape backing	Remove tape backing just prior to splice actuation.
	Allowing dust to accumulate on the tape	The best practice is not to remove the tape backing cover film until the splice is almost ready to occur. Not more than 10 minutes prior recommended.
Condition 8		
Slack in web while running or immediately core; after splicing	Paper roll over traveling	Check for insufficient braking force due to (1) low air pressure; (2) worn chucks; (3) worn brakes; (4) bad roll; or (5) automatic tension control not functioning as designed.

D. Corrugating Roll Defects

The condition of corrugating rolls and their operation have been generally overlooked in the corrugated industry. To cope with today's higher quality and production demands, more attention has to be given to corrugating roll condition. Properly operated, corrugating roll life may be prolonged as well as effecting a reduction of waste.

This section of the Fabrication Manual describes some of the more common corrugating roll defects and suggests remedies. Some of the techniques employed were outlined in a paper by H. J. Ostrowski and P. A. Gartaganis presented at the TAPPI 18th Testing Conference and 53rd Annual Meeting. The project was sponsored by the Process and Quality Control Committee of TAPPI's Corrugated Container Division under TAPPI CA 3041 and CA 3062.

Typical New Corrugating Roll Pressure Patterns

These illustrate typical new roll pressure patterns in A, B, and C flutes. The solid bars may be wider or narrower with slightly different spacings depending on make. The illustration also shows pressure patterns of existing corrugator rolls that are in parallel and under uniform pressure.

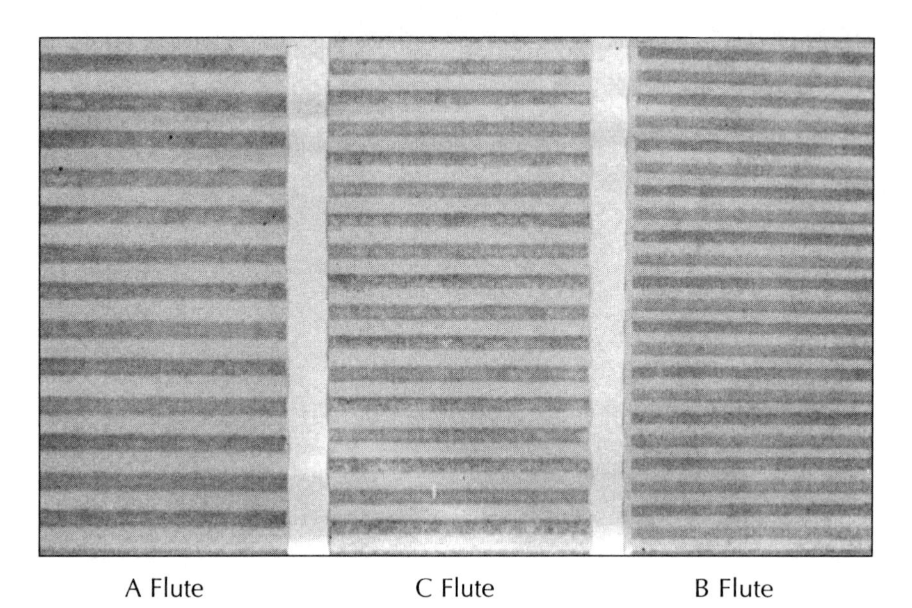

A Flute C Flute B Flute

Safety Precaution: Use extreme care when turning singlefacer on. To eliminate the possibility of injury, communicate with partner(s).

Corrugator roll pressure patterns are created by using a continuous strip of carbonless carbon paper from a roll of same. Typical size would be 8 1/2 x the width of the corrugator rolls as the length of the strip. With the corrugator hot and under pressure, introduce the strip between the upper and lower corrugating rolls arcross the full width of the corrugating rolls. Use assistance as required. Start up the singlefacer and remove the fluted strip as it exits the lower corrugator roll/pressure roll nip and examine the pattern.

NOTE 1: The singlefacer should be idled for several minutes before taking the sample to eliminate any out of round conditions caused by uneven heat distribution.

NOTE 2: In lieu of a continuous strip of carbonless carbon paper, three sandwiches of two sheets of 8 1/2 x 11 paper with conventional carbon paper in between can be used. They should be introduced simultaneously at the operator's side, center, and drive side of the corrugating rolls.

Uneven Corrugating Roll Nip Pressure Loading

These patterns illustrate a heavy pressure on the operator's side and a light pressure on the drive side. This causes non-uniform wear as well as variable quality convertibility across the sheet of combined board.

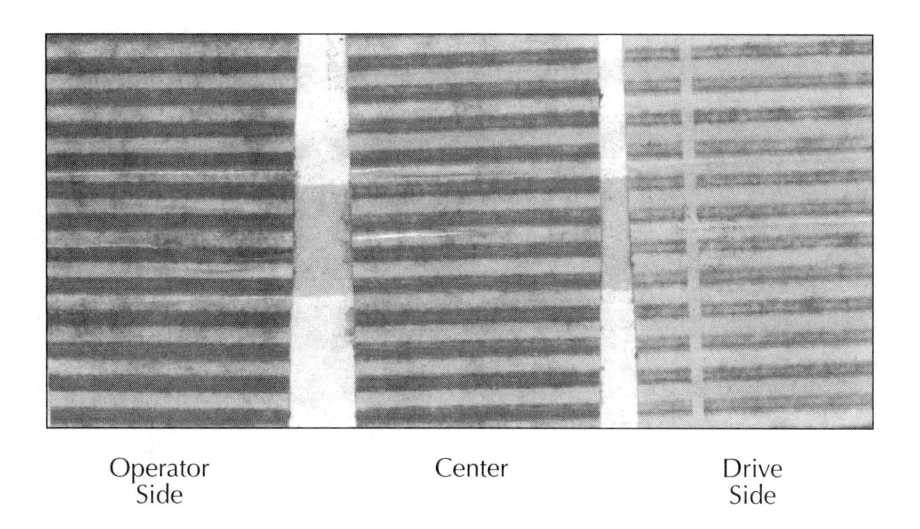

Operator Side | Center | Drive Side

Causes

Hydraulic, pneumatic, or manual pressure adjustment out of control

Loading gauges out of calibration.

Pressure cylinders malfunctioning.

Remedies

Adjust and equalize roll pressure.

Check and correct gauges.

Repair malfunction in pressure cylinders.

Uneven Corrugating Roll Nip Pressure—High in Center

These patterns illustrate a higher roll pressure in center than at both ends. This causes excessive wear in the center and variable convertibility across the sheet of combined board.

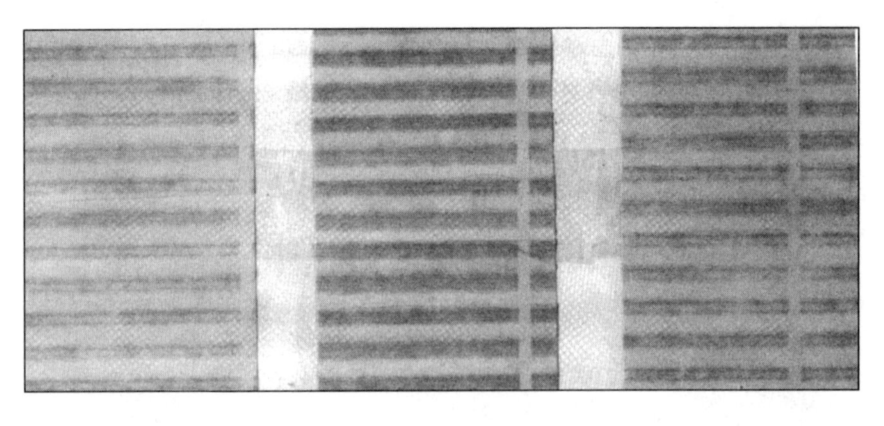

Operator Center Drive

Causes	Remedies
Incorrect crowning.	Replace rolls with correct crowns if necessary.
Incorrect end load pressure application.	Increase end load pressures.

Uneven Corrugating Roll Nip Pressure—Low in Center

These patterns illustrate uneven pressure with the center being low. This causes variable convertibility quality across the sheet of combined board.

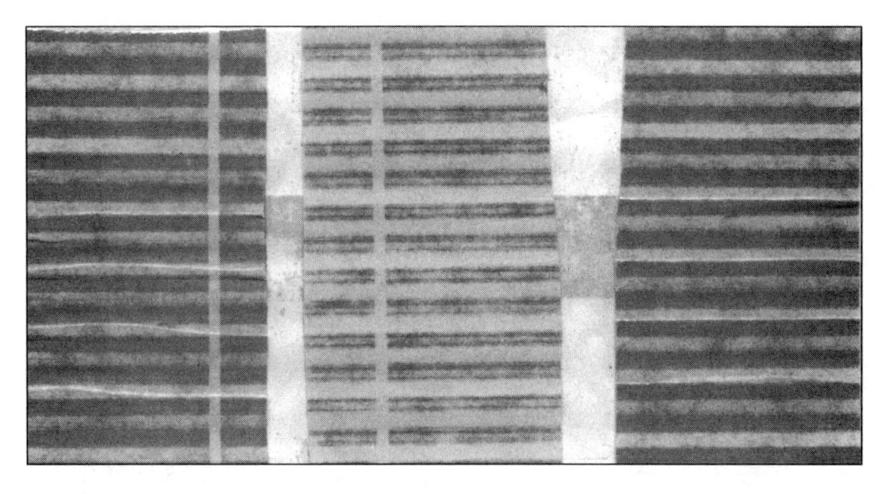

Operator Center Drive

Causes	Remedies
Incorrect crowning.	Replace rolls with correct crown if necessary.
Excessive wear in center.	Renew rolls if necessary.
Incorrect end load pressure application.	Check and correct end load pressures.

Misaligned—Corrugating Rolls Not Parallel

These patterns illustrate rolls out of alignment in which contact on one flank reverses from one end of the rolls to the other. Misalignment may also be on one end only. This causes excessive roll wear as well as develops an inherent tendency for the flutes to lean (see page 7).

Operator Center Drive

Causes

Roll(s) moves further out of adjustment during operation.

Paralleling mechanism not secure.

Remedies

Check and parallel rolls and source alignment adjustment.

Secure paralleling mechanism. Adjust to align.

Overall Corrugating Roll Wear

The pattern illustrates complete upper and lower roll contact on B flute. Medium fluted in this manner may not develop its full crush potential.

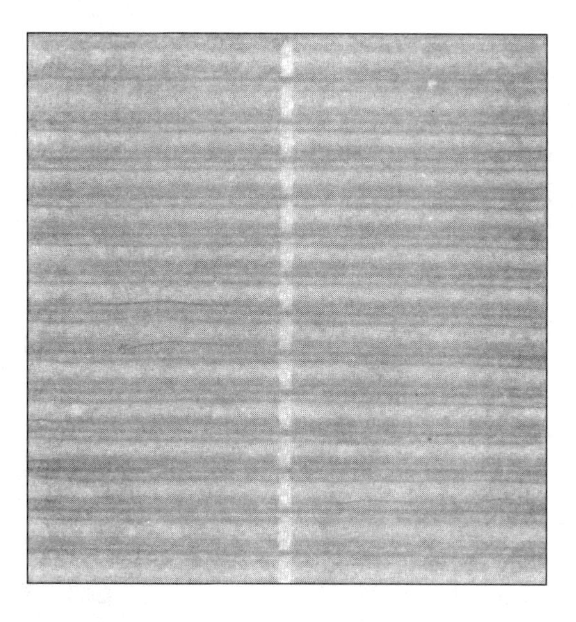

Cause

Rolls are approaching the end of their useful life.

Remedy

Replace rolls if necessary.

Worn Out Rolls

These C flute patterns illustrate the flank contact common for worn out rolls.

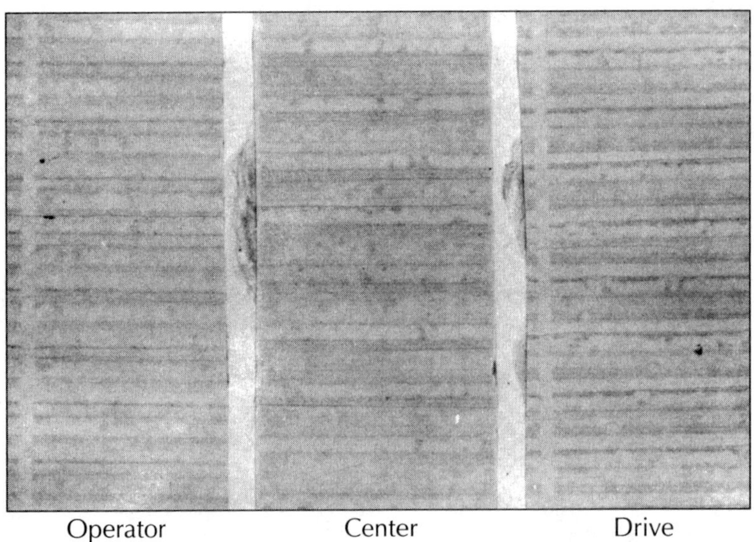

Cause

Running rolls beyond normal life.

Remedy

Replace rolls.

Excessive Wear Around Finger Slots Lower Corrugating Roll

The pattern in A flute illustrates excessive wear on the lower corrugating roll under the fingers. This makes it more difficult for the adhesive to form a continuous line and is one of the causes of finger lines.

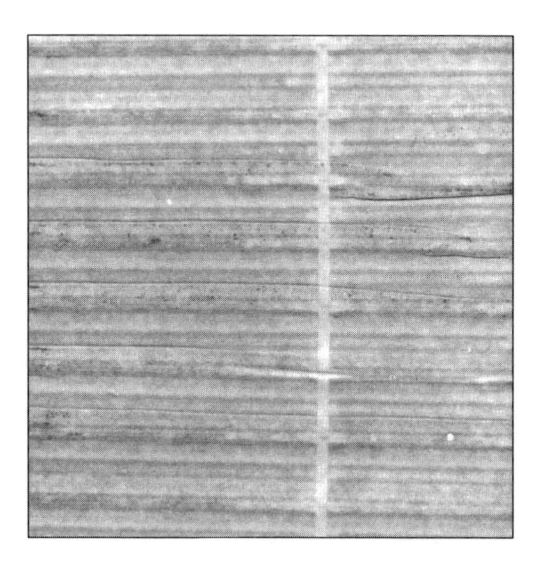

Causes	**Remedies**
Frequent improper finger adjustment. Fingers too tight.	Adjust and properly center fingers at all times.
Dirty fingers.	Clean fingers.
Crooked or improper fingers.	Straighten or replace fingers.

Pitted Corrugating Rolls

The pattern in A flute illustrates pits in the corrugating rolls. This may have slight adverse effect on combined board quality and may cause spotty adhesion.

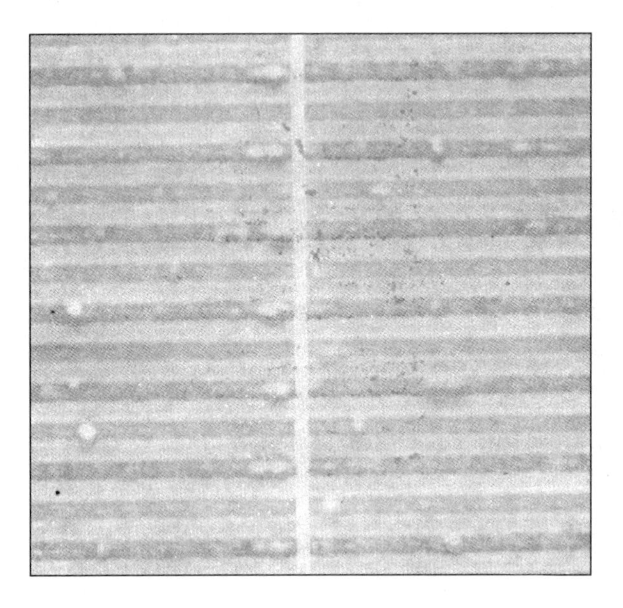

Cause

Foreign hard materials passing through rolls.

Remedies

Check medium for sand and foreign materials.
Keep foreign materials away from rolls.
Level raised blemishes by carefully grinding and polishing with a honing stone.

Dirty Corrugating Rolls

The pattern in C flute illustrates dirty corrugating rolls. This has a variable effect on combined board quality depending on the severity of contamination.

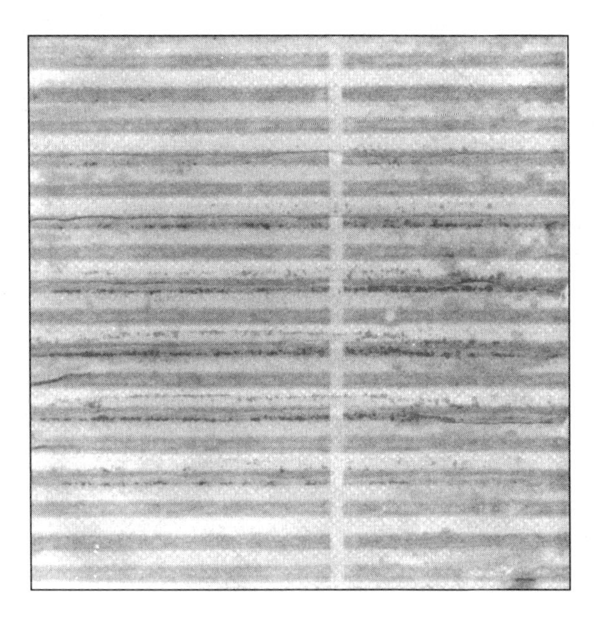

Causes	Remedies
Carbonizing of adhesive, fibers, and oil.	Clean with steam hose and apply light machine oil.
Accumulation of hardened starch adhesive.	Remove starch adhesive deposits.

Damaged Corrugating Rolls

The pattern illustrates one type of damage incurred by a set of B flute rolls.

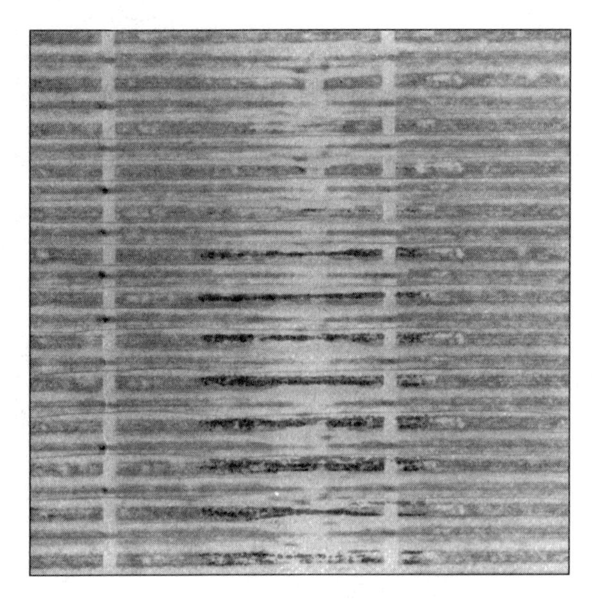

Cause

Hard metal object passing through rolls in operation.

Remedies

Avoid passing though any hard metal objects.
Replace roll if necessary.

Fractured or Cut Flutes

The pattern illustrates flutes cut or fractured. This lowers combined board flat crush and box compression depending on its severity (see page 28).

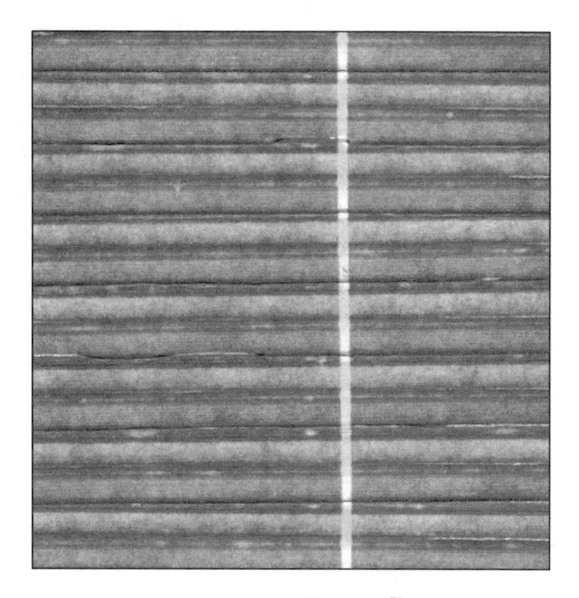

Causes	Remedies
Excessive medium web tension	
Machine components out of level/alignment causing loose edge/uneven tension on medium.	Check level/alignment of roll stand, preconditioner, and singlefacer.
Preconditioner not driven or driven under speed or preconditioner drum locked (will not rotate).	Repair/adjust drive mechanism.
Uneven or too much brake tension on medium.	Adjust brakes.
Splicer tension too high.	Lower splicer tension.
Medium	
Medium too dry.	Change roll if necessary.
Roll out of round or wound loose.	Use medium tension roll if possible. Change roll if necessary.
High coefficient of friction. Low MD tensile/stretch. Poor formation.	Use wax bar/oil mist. Change roll.
Preconditioning	
Lack of preconditioning.	Increase wrap and/or steam shower.
Preconditioning steam showers using 'dry' steam.	Repipe showers off return rather than high pressure steam.

Fractured or Cut Flutes

Continued

Causes	Remedies
Corrugating rolls	
Dirty corrugator rolls.	Clean rolls.
Rolls damaged or rough.	Hone rough surface or replace rolls.
Rolls out of parallel.	Parallel rolls.
Flute profile with low flank clearance. Can be an issue with thicker mediums (40# and higher).	Change to rolls with a relieved flank clearance ('modified' profile).

E: Visual Glue Line References

Singlefacer—Target

This photograph is intended to illustrate several things. First, the glue (starch) is where it belongs! The adhesive is placed in clearly defined lines. There is no displacement or smearing/slinging of adhesive. The parallel adhesive lines are about even in thickness and are not heavier on one side reflecting a good speed ratio. To the right side of the photograph, you can see an area where a finger line might occur. In this picture, the adhesive has properly filled in the potential (void) finger line creating a smooth strong glue line. The singlefacer glue lines have that "railroad track" appearance which indicates that the proper pressure has been applied to squeeze the starch from the glue tip out into two (2) distinct lines (too much pressure was not evident on this sample and can cause other problems.)

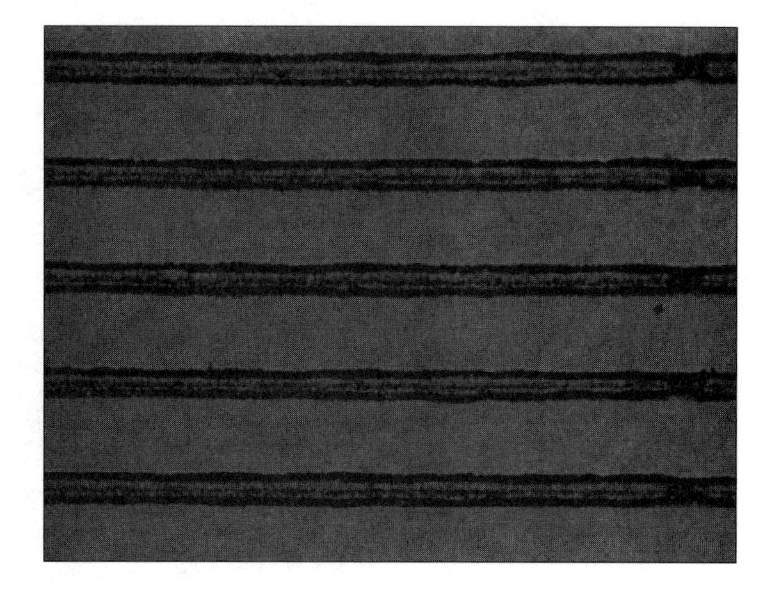

Singlefacer—Dirty Glue Roll, Wide Applicator Gap (Applicator Glue Roll to Lower Corrugator Roll)

This photograph represents two (2) major flaws as indicated by the heading. The glue roll is dirty and therefore not transferring adhesive properly. Some of this is seen by the large voids in the glue lines. The dirty areas on the glue roll will pick up less adhesive which is then wiped off, resulting in an inadequate amount left on the glue roll to transfer to the flute tips of the medium. The gap between the corrugator roll and the applicator glue roll is also too wide. This contributes to the spotty glue pattern seen in the photo. When this gap is too wide, the paper will again have an inadequate supply of adhesive transferred to it where it did not touch the glue roll. Please also note that the evenness of the glue line indicates a lack of pressure to squeeze the adhesive away from the flute tips (see target) and form the desired "railroad track" pattern. Box compression, ECT, and pin adhesion values will all be very low as a result of this glue pattern.

Singlefacer—Adhesive Slinging

Frequently, this is the result of low or high starch viscosity being run on a corrugator at fairly high speed. This condition can also result when the adhesive is too high in borax. Excessive borax can cause adhesive to "string" off of the glue roll. When the adhesive string "snaps", a bead of starch can be thrown onto the paper in a pattern like this photograph. If you look closely at the picture, you can also detect some speed ratio variation in that one of two (2) glue lines is slightly heavier than the other. This situation wastes adhesive.

Singlefacer—Finger Lines

This is a very common problem on fingered machines. It is also a serious problem for production, as it can result in box failure when boxes are loaded with product and in the field. Low compression scores typically result from boxes like this. Compression weakness will occur in the form of a major failure at these finger lines. A finger line is actually a very clearly defined dry streak. This may be caused by finger guides being bent, worn, not properly centered, or set too tight. Adhesive then accumulates on the finger guides and gels. This gelled starch then wipes the good adhesive (starch) off of the glue roll thereby creating a finger line or dry streak. Other possible causes of this condition include: wet medium, a wide groove in the transfer roll (wear related), or sometimes a wide groove in the left side of the photo to be wiped away from the glue roll.

Other problems seen on this photo include a noticeable speed ratio problem and the beginning of two (2) wet streaks. Something also caused the adhesive seen on the left side of the photo to be wiped away from the glue roll.

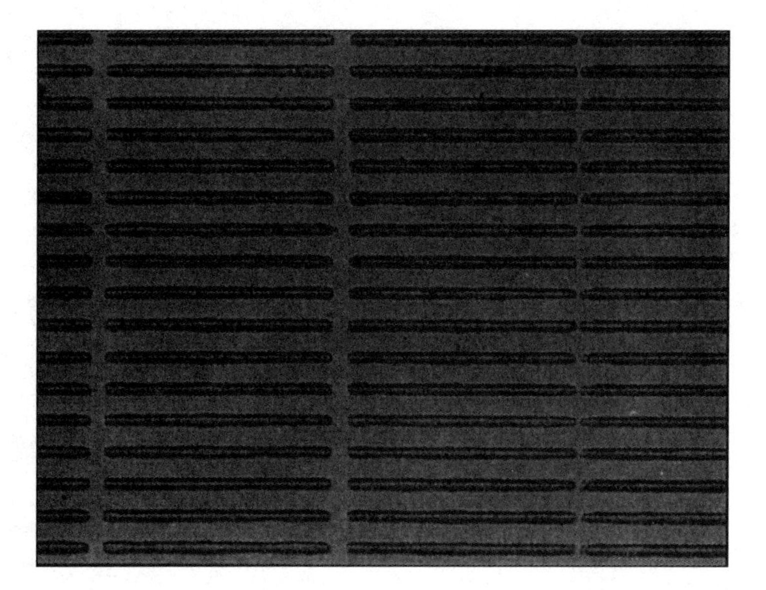

Singlefacer—Vacuum Lines

This may occur in a fingerless machine. This is the same general defect as a finger line except that it is caused by excessive vacuum being drawn on the slotted corrugator rolls. Too much vacuum will draw the medium up into the slots on the corrugator roll. The result of this is to dent the paper making it impossible to transfer adhesive to the flute tips. The resulting problems and box failures are the same as for finger lines.

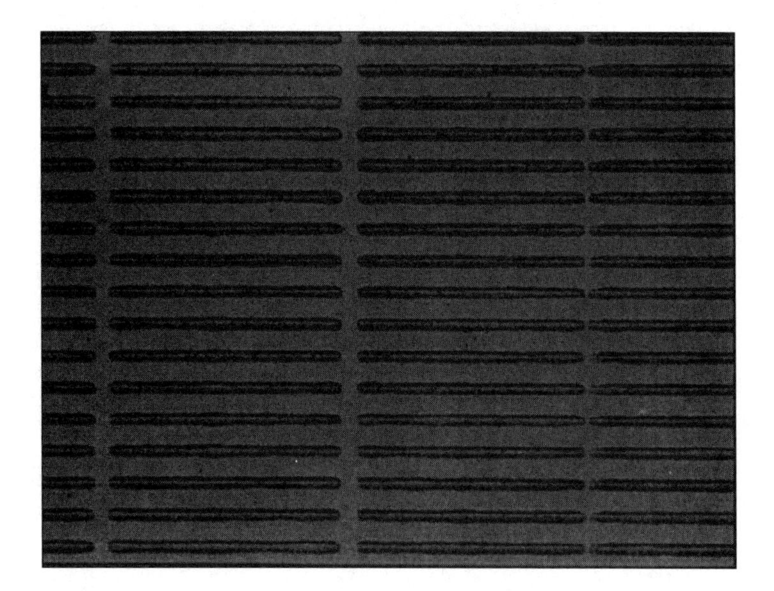

Singlefacer—Start of a Wet Streak/Wet Streaks

In this photograph (on the left side of the page), there is a small dry streak just to the left of the wet streak. The next photo on this page (to the right), is a full blown series of wet streaks. Wet streaks waste adhesive and may contribute to warp in light weight paper grades. Generally, a build up of gelled starch on finger guides or elsewhere acts like a wick and transfers adhesive that rubs off of it (the gelled starch) onto the medium. This creates a wet streak of wasted adhesive. If the gelled starch changes position, it can cause the opposite problem (a dry streak) by rubbing adhesive off of the glue roll.

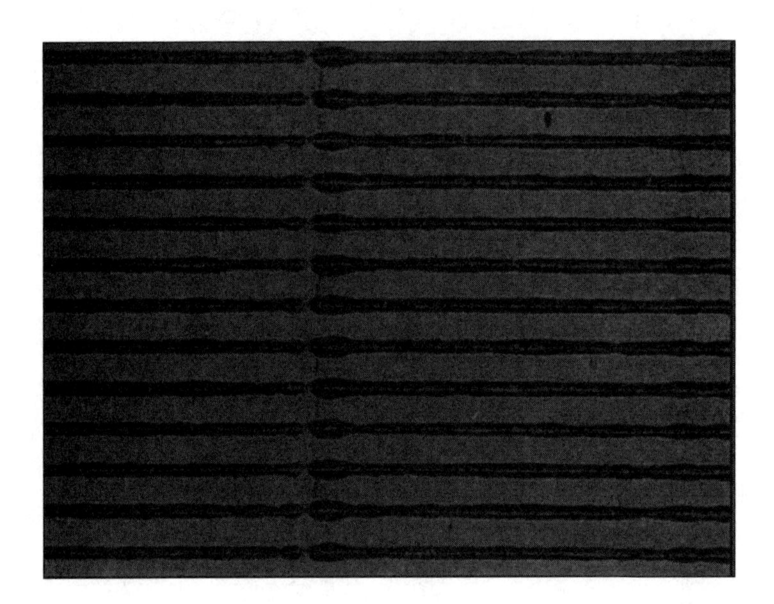

Singlefacer—Fluff Out

Fluff outs or blow outs can be found on both fingered and fingerless singlefacers. This particular example occurred before the glue roll. The board represented by this photo is all waste—it has no value except to a recycling mill. On a fingered machine, this situation can be caused by: finger guides being set too far away from the corrugator rolls; broken, bent or worn finger guides; wet medium; uneven pressure on the pressure roll; dirty corrugator rolls; loose brakes on the medium roll stand; and uneven or low pressure on the corrugator rolls.

On a fingerless machine, the above items not related to finger guides still apply. A loss of vacuum on the corrugator rolls—even momentarily—will also cause this.

Singlefacer—Speed Ratio (Over/Under Speed)

Speed ratio problems lead to adhesive being applied more heavily to one side of the flute tip rather than to the center of the flute tip (where it belongs). This results in the glue lines having a heavier track (or line) on the side of the flute that received the most adhesive.

The real problem with this is that the glue roll surface speed and the lower corrugator roll surface speed are not both running at the manufacturers specified speed ratio (they normally do not run at the exact same speeds). Low in adhesion values and a weak or one-sided bond may result from this condition as the adhesive being applied is not being positioned efficiently (leaving half of the bond weak).

Singlefacer—Light Glue Lines

This situation could be caused by tight fingers. The result is usually loose liner and/or low pin adhesion values. Compression scores will also be low as well ECT values.

Simply stated, there is not enough adhesive being applied to make a good bond. Other causes may include: glue roll set too close to the metering roll or blade, glue roll set too far away from the lower corrugation roll, or overly tight meter roll wiper blade pressure causing the meter roll to bow inward thus reducing the meter gap in the center.

Singlefacer—Heavy Glue Lines

This condition is the opposite of the one presented previously. In this case, too much adhesive is being applied. This situation wastes adhesive (and money), and may cause wash boarding and/or warp. Heavy glue lines are often the result of the glue roll being too far away from the metering roll or blade and abnormally high adhesive viscosity levels.

Singlefacer—Low Adhesive Viscosity

The low viscosity photo also reflects a speed ratio problem. If you look at the heavy lines outer edge and observe the waviness of it, you are seeing the effect of low viscosity. Low viscosity starch results in a watery paste (starch) which may yield poor pin adhesion, ECT's and compression test values.

Singlefacer—High Adhesive Viscosity

This photo has several deficiencies. The adhesive is being applied very heavily, thereby wasting adhesive. The primary problem, however, is the displacement (slinging) of adhesive. This situation is caused by, and typical of, high viscosity adhesive. The adhesive is so thick that it globs and is almost stringy in nature. This is why the adhesive that is being thrown between flute tips is stringy and globular in appearance. In severe situations, this could cause washboard, warp, and loss of board caliper/ECTs.

Doublebacker—Target

The adhesive is applied in a fairly smooth even line across the web. There is no slinging of adhesive or smearing of the glue lines present. The speed ratio, placement, and metering of adhesive are all good as is the adhesive viscosity.

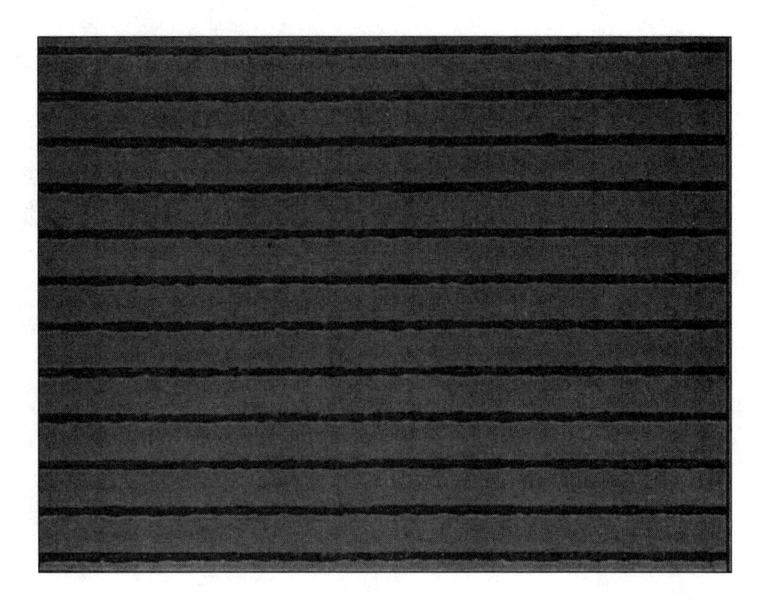

Doublebacker—Light Glue Lines

There is simply not enough adhesive being applied here. The end result will be low pin adhesions, ECT, and compression results. This may be caused by the metering roll being set too close to the glue roll, low adhesive viscosities, or the cells of the engraved applicator roll are clogged thus not transferring the desired amount of adhesive.

Doublebacker—Heavy Glue Lines

This situation is the opposite of light glue lines. An excessive amount of adhesive is being applied on this example. Adhesive is being wasted and may result in warped board. This may be caused by the metering roll being set too far away from the glue roll. Applicator glue roll to rider roll too tight smashing flutes into adhesive.

Doublebacker—Excessive Brake

This photograph represents a fairly specific problem—excessive roll stand brake being applied to the medium. In this case, the paper has so much tension applied to it that the top corrugator slots are appearing in the glue line pattern. This pattern is similar to both the finger line pattern and the light glue line pattern combined. The effect of this condition on a box will be poor pin adhesions, ECT's, and compression scores.

Doublebacker—Debris Wiping Starch

This photograph is indicative of its title. There is in fact debris wiping starch off of the glue roll.The debris may be paper, gelled starch, or some other foreign material. The results are predictable—severe compression failure of the carton. This condition may be visible from outside the carton as a streak of delamination.

Doublebacker—Low Viscosity Adhesive

This is illustrated by the wavy uneven glue line edges. Also, note that there is some smear to one side. Minor slinging of adhesive has also begun. Box performance will be questionable—it may be affected or may not. There are too many other variables on this one to make an accurate prediction.

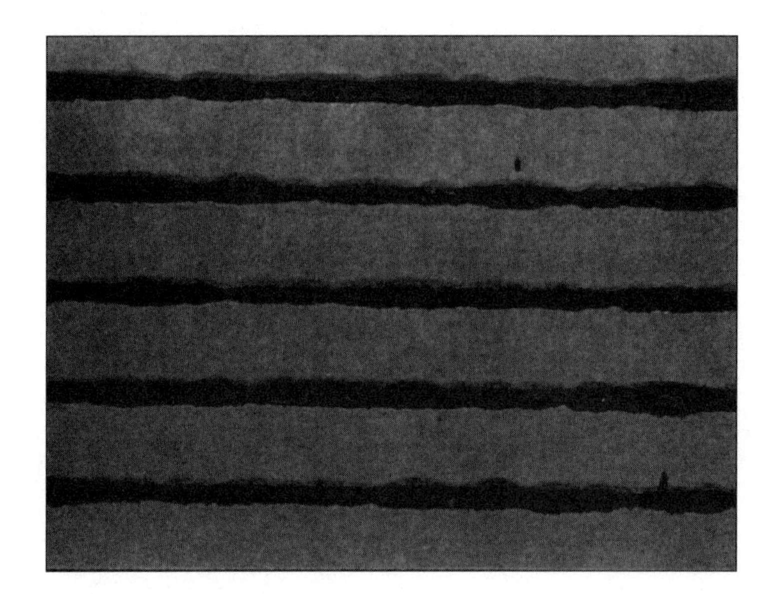

Doublebacker—Wide Gap—Rider to Glue Roll

This photo's glue lines look a little bit like high-lows, but aren't. The reason that this represents a gap problem is that the heaviest lines aren't really solid—the key here is the patterns inconsistency. The gap between these rolls is simply too wide, allowing the paper to make irregular contact with the glue roll. The results are: very low pin adhesions, ECT's and compression values.

Doublebacker—Speed Ratio (Over/Under)

Like the singleface, this means that adhesive is being applied heavier to one side of the flute tip (off center). Note that the glue line is much heavier on one side than the other. This can result in a directional pull situation where fiber pull is good in one machine direction, but zipper board results in the other. In this case, the surface speed of the applicator glue roll and the surface speed of the web are not the same.

If the speed ratio is greater than the manufacturer specifications, the applicator glue roll is running too fast (or the web too slow). This results in applying too much adhesive to the front edge of the flute. If the speed ratio is too slow, the reverse conditions will occur with a heavy glue line to the trailing edge of the flute tip.

Doublebacker—High Viscosity Adhesive—25 Quad Roll

This situation is known to come from a 25 quad applicator glue roll. These applicator glue rolls (25 quad) are used to better control the amount of adhesive being applied (lower application levels). When the adhesive is too thick, it doesn't transfer or flow well in these higher quad glue rolls. The end result is a spotty pattern. The results in box performance are low pin adhesion, ECT, and compression scores. For higher application levels or use of high viscosity adhesives most plants use a 16 quad applicator roll. Contact your roll supplier to help determine your requirements.

Doublebacker—Blow Outs

There are two (2) pictures of this shown because they almost appear to be opposites. The effect on boxes is severe delamination of the DB liner.

Possible causes include: dirty corrugator rolls, loss of rider roll pressure, ride roll bearing failure, brake tension problems, and bridge guide problems. Another major possible cause would be fluff outs or blow outs at the singlefacer.

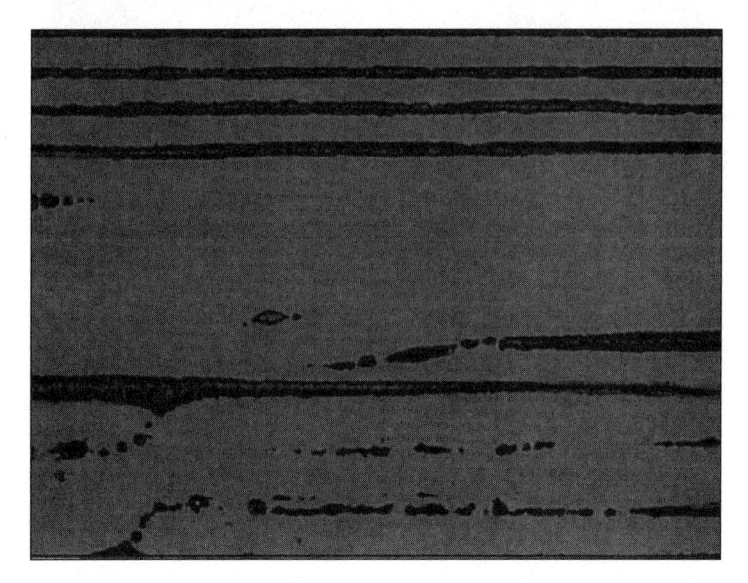

Doublebacker—High Lows

High lows are produced at the singlefacer but result in irregular glue patterns on the doubleface liner side. They are caused by poor control of the medium from the corrugator roll nip point to the pressure roll nip point (or on newer machines, the point at which it is bonded to the singleface liner). This lack of control (by fingers on older machines or by pressure differential on newer machines) allows flutes to distort. The picture on this page shows the telltale 'high-low' glue pattern on a sample of doubleface liner from combined corrugated board that has been soaked apart and stained with a weak solution of iodine. The low or distorted flutes either fails to transfer their adhesive to the liner or do not pick up enough adhesive.

High lows adversely affect bonding and therefore negatively impact pin adhesion tests, flat crush, ECT (Edge Crush Test), and stacking strength (top-to-bottom compression). Operators often try to correct high lows by increasing double adhesive application and rider roll pressure. This causes caliper loss and can result in warp and wet board.

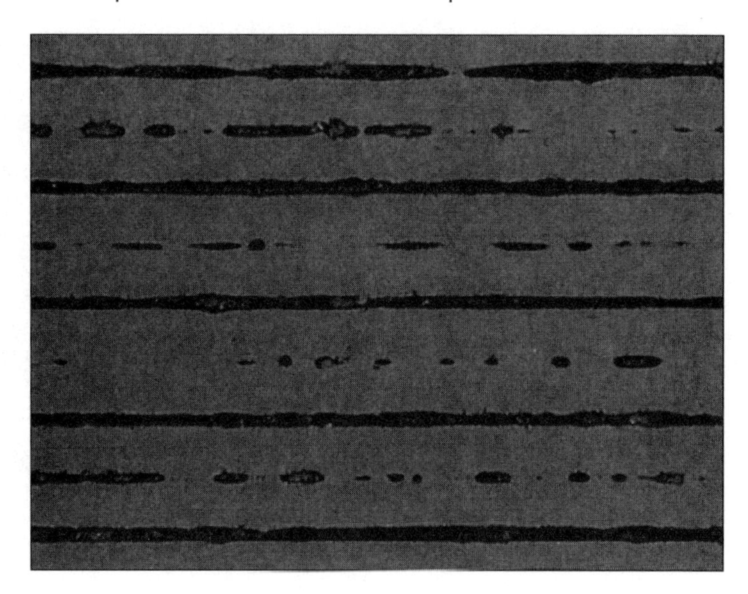

Doublebacker—Adhesive Slinging

This situation appears to represent a low adhesive viscosity which was then run at a high speed. As seen earlier, watery, low viscosity adhesive produces light glue lines. The displaced adhesive in non-stringy—a sure sign of low viscosity adhesive. A high borax content in the adhesive may also cause the starch to string off of the glue roll. The low viscosity can then counteract the effect of the borax to a degree leaving a non-stringy pattern. Excessive slinging can also result from missing or inadequate glue machine splash guards. This can also cause warp and/or wet board if severe enough. The result on box test scores is low pin adhesion, ECT's, and compressions. Zipper board and loose liner are also possible.

Doublebacker—Bridge Web Tension

These photos illustrate the result from improperly setting the bridge web guides. The guides may be too tight and/or not aligned properly. The result is that the web is then pulled to one side and is therefore bouncing when it makes contact with the glue roll. This torque on the bouncing web causes the double glue line pattern (offset). The box made from this board may experience lower than usual pins, ECT's, and compression depending on the severity of the problem.

Part 2: Printing Problems

A. Printing Defects
B. Sample Anilox Rolls

Most printing problems are common to both flexographic and paste ink printing presses. Whenever the noted problems or remedies are unique to one process or the other, a notation is provided.

A. Printing Defects

Dimensions—Incorrect

Refers to the incorrect length and width of sheet, position of scores, and location of plates.

Causes	Remedies
Trim knife or score(s) positioned incorrectly.	Relocate knife or score(s) to correct position.
Print copy not positioned correctly after trim knife or score(s) has/have been relocated.	Relocate plates according to correct trim or scoreline(s).
Trim knife heads and/or score heads coming loose during run.	Relocate head(s) and tighten down firmly (manually set-up machines). Investigate and repair root cause. • Trim and/or slotting head(s) worn from many years of use. • Locking mechanism not working properly.

Printing Plates—Incorrect Layout

Refers to the improper location and mounting of the various printing plates.

Causes	Remedies
Print content or location of plates incorrectly mounted as a set.	Check print copy and dimensions on all plates mounted as a set prior to releasing for use on a printer-slotter, flexo folder gluer or flexo rotary die cutter.
Print copy positioned incorrectly on press (individual sections or segments of print copy).	Recheck setup and relocate any plate that is incorrectly positioned.

Printing Plates—Poor Condition

Refers to physical conditions such as scratches, torn places, and worn letters.

Causes	Remedies
Plates worn excessively or have hardened.	Replace plates.
Uneven wear.	Remount plates using "build-up" techniques (or replace individual sections of the mount). Use a mounter-proofer to ensure finished mount is within desired thickness specifications.
Worn backing.	Remount plates.

Poor Definition

Refers to poor legibility or clarity of outline of printed matter.

Causes	Remedies
Printing plates not uniform in thickness.	Replace defective printing plate.
Excessive print pressure.	Use only enough print cylinder/impression cylinder clearance to prevent smear.
Excessive ink application.	Reduce ink application.
Dirty printing plates.	Clean printing plates.
Excessive pressure between form rollers and printing plates (paste ink presses only).	Increase clearance between form rollers and printing plate.
Haloing (flexo presses only).	See page 124.

Distorted Image

Refers to an unintended distortion of the printed image.

Causes

Excess printing pressure.

Printing plates manufactured without appropriate compensation for "stretch" (particularly for printing accurate circles.)

Remedies

Reduce pressure.

Obtain properly made replacement printing plates.

Register

Refers to placement of printing at the various locations on the sheet where two or more colors are in close proximity to one another. Can also include print jobs when overprint overlap is not equal, or unacceptable variation between print copy and the flap scores even on one color print jobs.

Causes	Remedies
Pull rolls not adjusted properly on multicolor printer-slotter.	The pull rolls for each succeeding color should be a little tighter than the one preceding to achieve equal pressure on all colors due to a slight reduction in caliper of the board as sheets are pulled through the printing press.
Print cylinder(s) not timed properly.	Check to determine which color is out of register. Adjust one color at a time.
Feed and pull rolls worn excessively.	Replace worn rolls.
Printing plate manufactured incorrectly to achieve proper register.	Check all printing plates when received. Printing plates must be manufactured to allow overprint overlap to be uniform on overprint areas when plates are properly mounted.
Printing plate mounted incorrectly.	Re-mount plates to provide for proper register. Use a mounter-proofer to ensure proper registration.
Mechanical condition of tire press (gear, keyway, and/or shaft wear).	Perform appropriate maintenance up to and including a major gear train rebuild to bring press within register capabilities required by customers.
Insufficient sheet control.	Adjust nip points (including parallel). Add pull bands.
Excessively warped board.	Back bend flaps if allowed and if possible. Re-run order on corrugator.
Improper or non-use of pull bands.	Use proper height pull bands correctly placed.
Sheet too narrow for the press.	Switch job to smaller press.

Printing Crush

Refers to an excessive amount of crush of corrugations due to pressure applied by printing plates to the container.

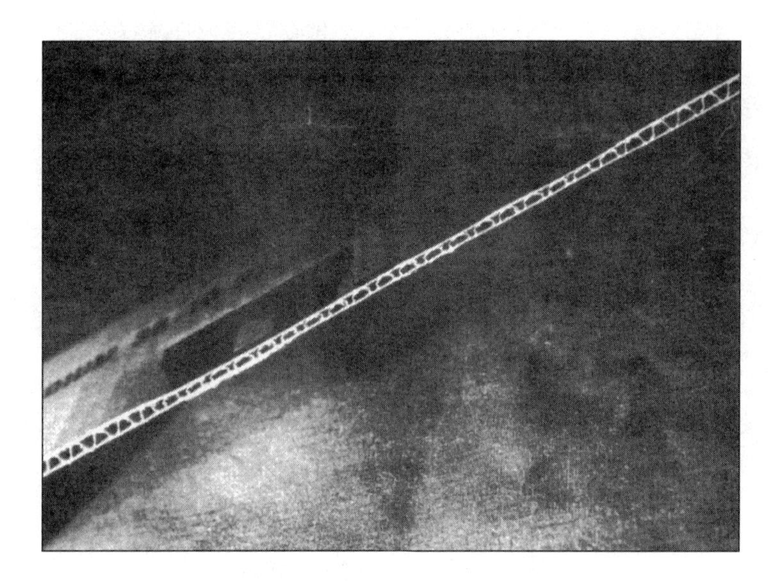

Causes	Remedies
Excessive print cylinder pressure.	Increase print cylinder/impression cylinder clearance.
Uneven or improper printing plate backing.	Replace printing plate backing. Use a mounter-proofer to ensure over all plate caliper specifications are achieved.
Uneven printing plate wear.	Re-mount printing plates using appropriate build-up technique (and replace pieces or sections of print copy, if necessary). Use a mounter-proofer to ensure overall printing plate caliper specifications are achieved.
Excessive pull band pressure.	Increase (open) gap between printing cylinder and impression cylinder if print quality is not compromised.
Oversized pull bands.	Install correct thickness pull bands.

Ink—Non Standard Colors and Shades

Refers to the non-uniformity of color intensity and shade with respect to the standard.

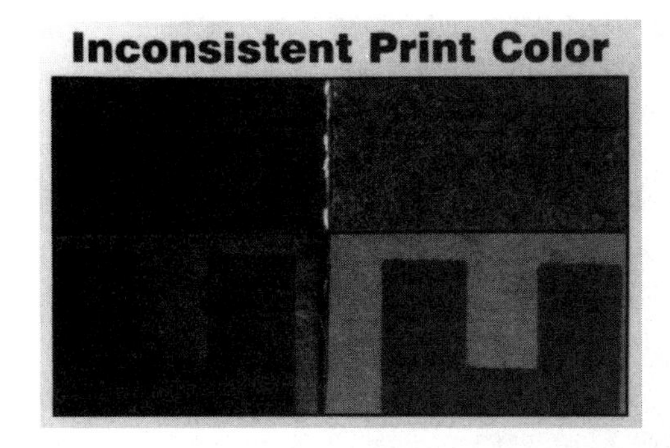

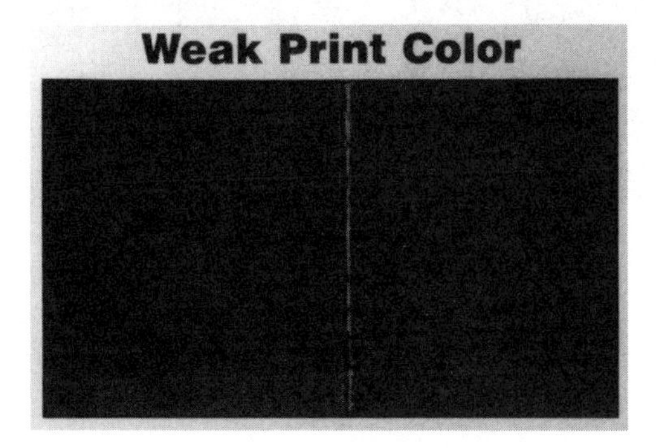

Causes	Remedies
Incorrect ink formulation.	Check each batch of ink with standard color swatch, densitometer or spectrophotometer. Replace ink with correct color.
Incomplete cleaning of inking system from previous job.	Remove ink from system, clean system and replace with fresh ink.
Using incorrect color.	Use the correct ink color.
Incorrect viscosity, ink not thoroughly mixed, or ink improperly formulated.	Check viscosity. On long runs, repeat every half hour. Adjust viscosity and thoroughly circulate ink through press three to five minutes before printing. Consult ink supplier to formulate ink to run on press between 20 and 25 seconds.
Water getting into ink, valve sticking on automatic washup device.	Check water shutoff valve, (piston may stick). Increase air supply to correct.

Ink—Poor Coverage

Refers to the improper intensity and amount of printing ink applied to a sheet.

Flexographic Printing Only

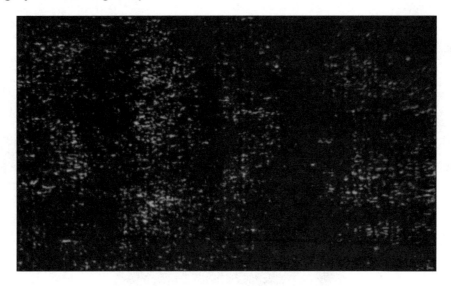

Causes	Remedies
Improper adjustment of wiper roll.	Adjust wiper roll.
Wiper roll worn excessively.	Replace wiper roll.
Improper adjustment of wiper blade.	Adjust wiper blade.
Wiper blade worn excessively.	Replace wiper blade.
Anilox roll dirty.	Clean anilox roll.
Anilox roll worn excessively or has an improper ink cell column capacity.	Replace anilox roll.
Anilox roll pressure too light.	Decrease anilox roll to printing cylinder gap.
Damaged anilox roll.	Replace anilox roll.
Substrate not accepting ink or not accepting ink uniformly.	Seek assistance from paper mill and/or ink manufacturer's technical representative.
Washboard stock.	Reduce print cylinder/impression cylinder clearance or re-run board off the corrugator.
Ink viscosity too low.	Add or replace ink using ink from a new container.
Printing plate surface glazed.	Clean or replace printing plates.
Improper printing plate durometer.	Check with platemaker for proper durometer.
Too little plate impression.	Increase plate to substrate impression.

Ink—Poor Coverage

(Continued)

Flexographic Printing Only

Causes	Remedies
Ink film too thin for substrate characteristics (i.e. too rough, too porous).	Increase ink film thickness by: Raising ink viscosity. Decreasing metering of anilox roll. Increasing anilox roll volume. Ink reformulation for substrate.
Printing plate too hard.	Use plates with a softer durometer.
Substrate surface finish resists ink wetting.	Consult ink supplier for product or additive recommendations.
Ink drying too fast.	Slow drying by adding slow solvents. Eliminate air or heat blowing on plates. Increase machine speed.
Ink pH too low.	Check and adjust ink pH to specification.
Low spots in printing plates.	Build up printing plates in low areas. Replace printing plates.
Out-of-parallel condition between one or more of the critical nip points.	Check parallel and adjust as necessary.

Ink—Poor Coverage

(Continued)

Paste Ink Printing Only

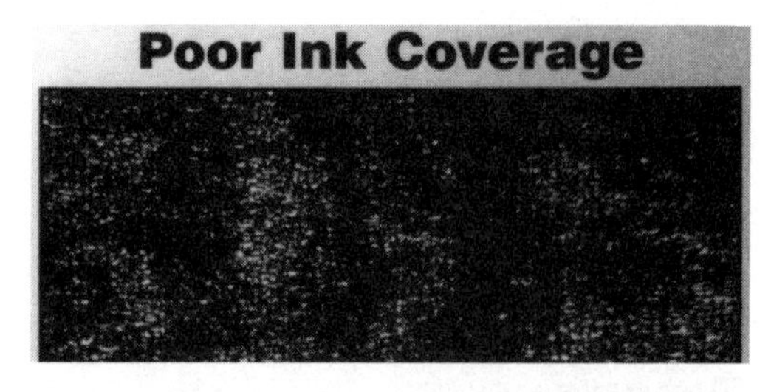

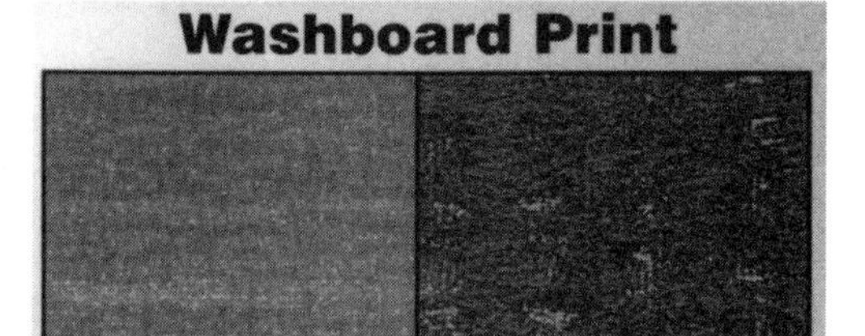

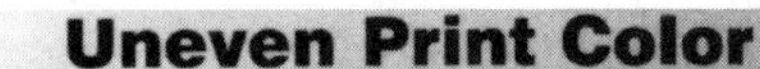

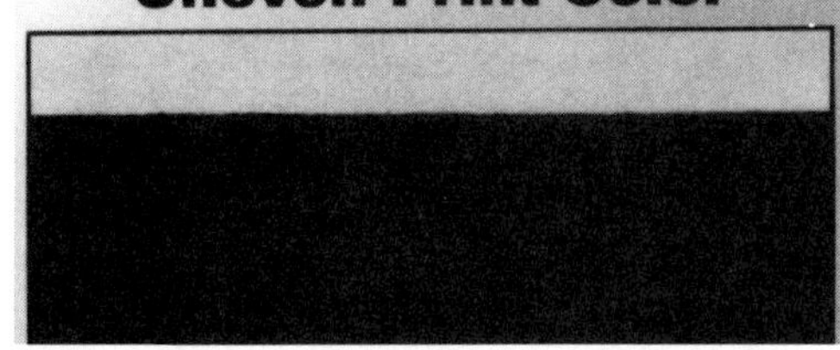

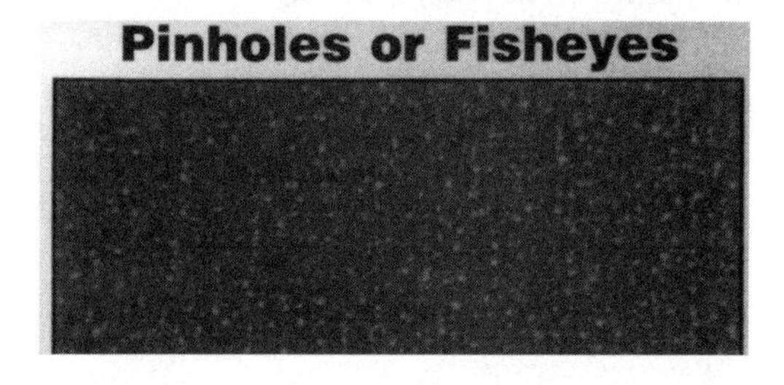

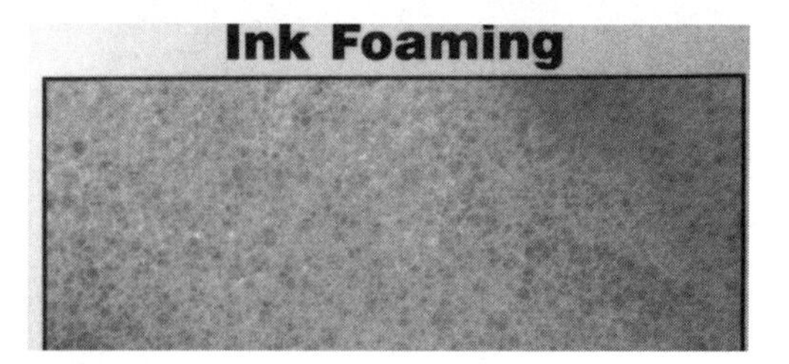

Causes	Remedies
Unevenly adjusted form rollers causing uneven ink distribution across press.	Adjust form rollers for even pressure across rollers.
Fountain keys improperly adjusted causing an excessive or light ink application.	For optimum conditions, increase ink flow by adjusting fountain keys until minimum amount is being used that will provide good coverage.
Washboard stock.	Reduce print cylinder/impression cylinder clearance or re-run board off the corrugator.
Both form rolls not in use.	Use both form rolls.

Ink—Poor Coverage

(Continued)

Paste Ink Printing Only

Causes	Remedies
Damaged ink roll(s) in ink roll stack.	Replace damaged ink roll(s).
Printing plate surface glazed.	Clean or replace plate.
Improper printing plate durometer.	Check with platemaker for proper durometer.
Low spot in printing plate(s).	Build up printing plates in low areas. Replace printing plates.

Poor Trapping/Overprint

Refers to the color intensity of the printing at the various places on the sheet where one color overlaps another.

Causes	Remedies
Incorrect ink sequence—i.e. trying to cover a darker color with a lighter color (flexo presses only).	Change printing color sequence if possible.
Excessive ink application.	Reduce ink application to achieve good coverage with a minimum amount of ink.
Ink colors and ink tack improperly selected (paste ink presses only).	Lighter color must be first down and must have more tack than second down color.
First down ink not dry due to ink problems or wet ink film thickness.	Increase drying speed of ink by: Reducing first down ink viscosity. Reducing ink film with better metering. Changing ink formulation for faster drying. Decreasing machine speed. Decreasing anilox volume. Increasing dryer(s) temperature.
Second down ink not printing due to low viscosity.	Increase second down ink viscosity to higher than that of first down ink.

Poor Trapping/Overprint

(Continued)

Causes	Remedies
Second down ink not printing due to ink drying too fast.	Slow drying down by: Adding slow solvents. Stopping air or heat blowing on plates. Increasing machine speed.
Second down ink not printing due to low or high pH.	Adjust ink pH to specifications (consult ink supplier) or replace with fresh ink.
Inks not drying due to high holdout of substrate.	Change substrate, reduce ink film thickness, or increase drying capacity.
Second down ink not compatible with first down ink.	Consult ink supplier for ink revisions, additives or product recommendations.

Offset

Refers to the quantity of ink visible on the inside of the container.

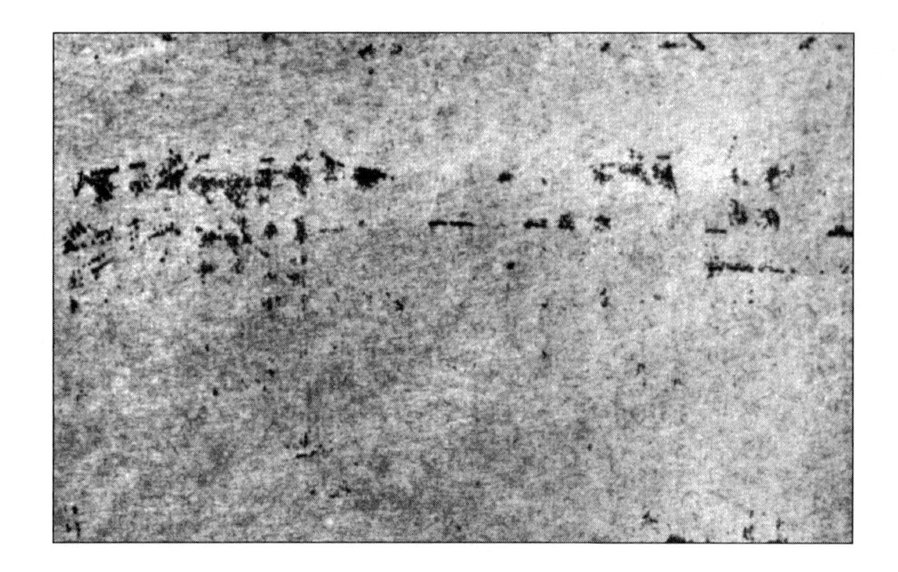

Causes	Remedies
Excessive ink application.	Reduce ink application. Paste ink printing offset can be caused or promoted by the normal weight of printed sheets in stacks. In these cases, offset can be minimized by reducing the stack height at the stacker and/or at in-process storage.
Insufficient drying capabilities of ink.	Seek assistance from ink manufacturer's technical representative. Paste ink printing offset can be caused or promoted by the normal weight of printed sheets in stacks. In these cases, offset can be minimized by reducing the stack height at the stacker and/or at in-process storage.
Inability of substrate to accept ink.	Re-run order with different outside liner, ink, or seek assistance from ink and/or liner manufacturer's technical representative(s).

Ink Smearing/Tracking

Occurs when printing ink is not kept within intended boundaries.

Causes	Remedies
Ink not dry due to ink or wet ink film thickness (excess ink application).	Increase drying speed of ink by: Reducing ink viscosity. Reducing ink film with better metering. Changing ink formulation for faster drying. Decreasing machine speed. Decreasing anilox volume. Increasing dryer(s) temperature.
Inks not drying due to high hold-out of substrate.	Change substrate, reduce ink film thickness, or increase drying capacity. Consult with paper manufacturer's and/or ink manufacturer's technical representative(s).
Insufficient drying capabilities of ink.	Seek assistance from ink manufacturer's technical representative.
Ink formulation.	Consult ink supplier's technical representative for recommendation.

Ink Smearing/Tracking

(Continued)

Uneven ink film applications on substrate (halos, uneven color).	Adjust ink metering rolls, print cylinder, anilox roll (flexo only) and impression cylinder parallel Check plate level. Also see "Haloing", page 124.
Dirty printing plates.	Clean printing plates.
Pull collars improperly set-in line with print copy.	Re-locate pull collars to be in-line with unprinted areas or, preferably, relocate to outside extremities of the corrugated sheet.
Worn or slipping folding belts. Guides, rails, or bars hitting print. Stacker belts hitting print.	Replace or adjust folding belts. Adjust or remove to minimize impact. Move or lift belts from print areas.
Machine attachments smearing ink.	Adjust sheet deflectors or delivery conveyor speed. If ink coverage is heavy, it may be necessary to increase speed of delivery conveyor for single delivery rather than shingling.
Die cut or folding operations: Worn or rough anvil blankets. Excessive cutting die pressure.	Optimize converting operations by: Replace or trim/grind anvil blankets. Remove die rubber, replace knives, reduce die pressure, replace anvil blankets. Consider the following: • Faster drying ink. • High intensity ink using a thinner film. • Two-press operation. • Use of the rotary score on the die cutter instead of scores on the cutting die. • Re-design to keep print copy away from die cut score line. • Replace scores with perforated score.
Improper sizes of one or more rolls or cylinders on the printing press causing an improper circumferential speed relationship between the cylinder(s) and the corrugated board.	Analyze all roll and cylinder diameters and replace (if required) with rolls and/or cylinders meeting manufacturer's specifications.
Printing plates picking up excessive ink prior to boxes entering printing section.	Place ink roll selector switch in DOWN position. Place it in AUTO position when blanks are ready to be printed.
Too much tack on first-down color of a two-color, or more, job.	First-down color must be formulated so that the tack at time of impression will not pick board. Viscosity (Flexo press only) of successive colors should be graduated with first-down color drying faster than second.
Ink throwing at high speed on print cylinder.	Cut down ink flow.

Dirty Printing

Fiber dust piling on edges of printed images.

Causes	Remedies
Dry and dusty board.	Get liner with better surface finish. More frequent stopping for cleaning of printing plates. Add vacuum capabilities to printing press to remove dust and paper fiber particles.
Ragged slitter edge.	Adjust or sharpen slitter knives.
Excessive plate impression.	Reduce plate to substrate impression.
Ink pH too low. (Flexo only).	Check and adjust ink pH to specification.
Excessive anilox to plate pressure. (Flexo only).	Adjust to reduce anilox impressions, check plate level.
Unlevel, worn, cupped, glazed or mismatched (slugged) plates.	Level, build up, clean, or replace plates or entire mount.

Dirty Printing

(Continued)

Causes	Remedies
Ink film too thick.	Reduce ink film thickness by: Lowering ink viscosity. Increasing ink metering effectiveness. Decreasing anilox volume.
Ink drying too fast.	Slow drying by adding solvents. Eliminate air or heat blowing on plates, or newly printed surfaces. Increase machine speed.
Uneven ink film applications due to machine or unlevel plates.	Adjust ink metering, print and anilox impressions, roll parallel, replace plates.
Printing plate(s) too soft.	Use plates with a harder durometer.
Inadequate ratio of dot sizes (print screen) to anilox roll cell count.	Revise artwork and printing plates to match press capabilities.

Ink Fill In

Fill-in of small type or design.

Causes	Remedies
Ink viscosity too high (Flexo presses).	Reduce viscosity.
Insufficient metering of ink film on anilox roll (Flexo presses).	Check with machinery manufacturer for recommended material or practice.
Excess ink application.	Reduce ink application.
Dirty printing plates.	Clean printing plates.
Excessive plate impression.	Reduce plate to substrate impression.
Unlevel, worn, cupped, glazed, or mismatched (slugged) plates.	Level, build up, clean, or replace plates or entire mount.
Ink film too thick for plate and art design.	Reduce ink film thickness by: Lowering ink viscosity. Increasing ink metering effectiveness. Decreasing anilox volume.

Ink Fill In

(Continued)

Causes	Remedies
Positive or reverses, too small for ink film thickness/metering.	Revise art, screens, and plates for press capabilities.
Ink drying too fast.	Slow drying by adding slow solvents. Eliminate air or heat blowing on plates. Increase machine speed.
Uneven ink film applications due to machine or unlevel plates.	Adjust ink metering, print and anilox impressions, roll parallel, replace plates.
Printing plate too soft.	Use plates with a harder durometer.
Foreign matter or specks of ink pigment in ink.	Strain ink or replace ink.
Paper dust from corrugated board and/or plant atmosphere.	More frequent stopping for cleaning printing plates. Add vacuum capabilities to printing press. Re-run order using liner with better surface finish.

Ink Voids

Voids in printing.

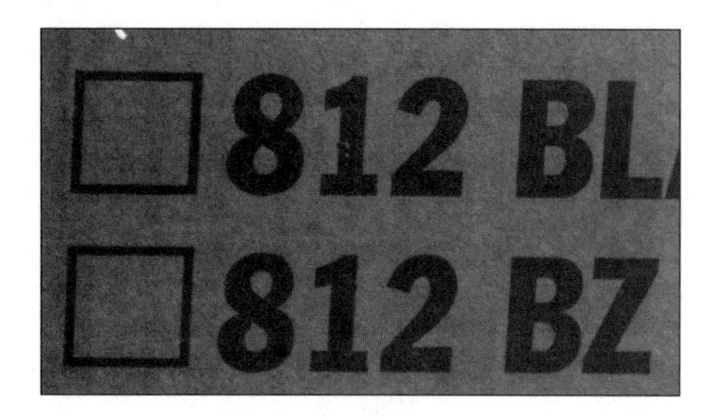

Causes	Remedies
Voids in printing plates (usually damage).	Replace printing plates or sections on printing copy.
Indentations in corrugated board.	Re-run order off corrugator. Corrugator belt lacing marks or a build-up of foreign material on the lower corrugator belt are typical causes. If the condition is not too severe, reducing the print cylinder/impression cylinder gap is an option. However, the indentations are usually deep enough so that adding printing plate impression to remedy the defect will cause unacceptable print crush.
Substrate not accepting ink uniformly.	Consult with paper manufacturer's or ink manufacturer's technical representative.

Incorrect Printing Copy

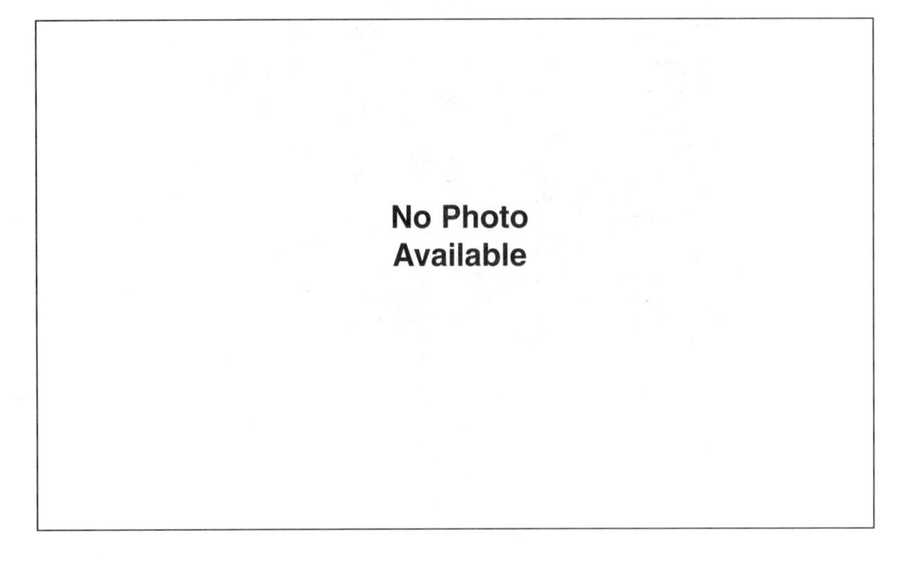

Causes

Printing plates incorrect (do not match factory order).

Customer changed print copy with a failure in the order entry process to notify production and obtain a new set of printing plates.

Remedies

Obtain correct set of printing plates.

Invariably it will be the customer who will discover the problem. Customer acceptance "as is" or with overprint and concession is a possibility. Re-running the order correctly is the usual remedy.

Print Askew

Print copy skewers with respect to the box blank.

No Photo
Available

Causes	Remedies
Unequally worn pull collars.	Replace pull roll collars.
Pull collar nip greater (wider gap opening) than in preceding section.	Tighten nip. Pull collar nips should be a few thousandths tighter as the sheet moves through the machine to pull properly.
Pull collar's underside dirty, changing diameter of pull collars.	Remove and clean periodically (minimum of every two weeks); color code to keep sets together.
Sheet kicker not set up correctly.	Adjust feed mechanism so that the sheet is introduced correctly into the press.
Print stop(s) dragging on one side or the other.	Adjust front stops so that sheet is fed into the press without skewing.
Pull bands pulling unevenly.	Replace pull bands so that pulling is easier.
Out-of-parallel condition with feed roll or pull collar shafts or between printing and impression cylinders.	Check parallel and correct as required.

Haloing
(Flexo Presses Only)

Halo around entire perimeter of print copy segments or on lead edge of printing.

Causes	Remedies
Entire image halos only:	
Halos around entire perimeter on print copy segments is typically caused by excess anilox roll to printing plate pressure.	Open the gap (reduce pressure) between the anilox roll and the print cylinder.
Lead edge halos only:	
Halo at lead edge of print copy segments is typically caused by excess pressure between the printing cylinder and the corrugated board.	Open the gap (reduce pressure) between the print cylinder and the impression cylinder.
Plate wrap distortion.	Use thinner plate materials compensating with backing build-up to maintain proper total thickness of plates and backing.
Loose plate or mount on cylinder.	Remount plate(s) to fit cylinder tightly.
Lead/trail edge halos only:	
Excessive anilox to plate impression.	Adjust to reduce anilox impressions, check plate level and mounting.
All halos:	
Unlevel, worn, cupped, glazed, or mismatched (slugged) plates.	Level, build up, clean, or replace plates or entire mount.
Uneven ink film applications due to machine or unlevel plates.	Adjust ink metering, print and anilox impressions, roll parallel, replace plates.
Ink film too thick/excessive ink.	Reduce ink film thickness by: Lowering ink viscosity. Increasing ink metering effectiveness. Decreasing anilox volume.
Printing plate too hard.	Use plates with softer durometer.

Striations (Flexo Presses Only)

Fine, but visible, regularly spread lines in the machine direction of a flexo printing press.

Causes	Remedies
Hydraulic action of ink in the presence of the anilox and meter roll in a 2-roll Flexo ink system. Note: True striations only exist in a Flexo press with a 2-roll ink system.	Reduce the hydraulic pressure by reducing the volume of ink in the anilox roll/meter roll nip. • Parabolically crown the meter roll to provide for a more uniform ink film across the anilox roll. • Reduce ink viscosity. • Replace the anilox roll with one that has small grooves between the cells. • Replace the meter roll with a blade system. Note: The first three remedies will only reduce striations. Only converting to a blade system will eliminate striations.
Visible lines can occur in a blade/anilox roll system but are of various widths and are irregularly spaced when compared with striations in a 2-roll ink system. These lines are not striations as striations do not occur in a blade/anilox roll system. Causes are typically chipped wiper blades or particles of dried ink or paper dust at the blade/anilox nip area.	Replace wiper blade. Clean debris from the blade/anilox nip area.

Washboard Print (Flexo Presses Only)

Small, irregularly sized, but frequently appearing parts of the substrate clearly visible.

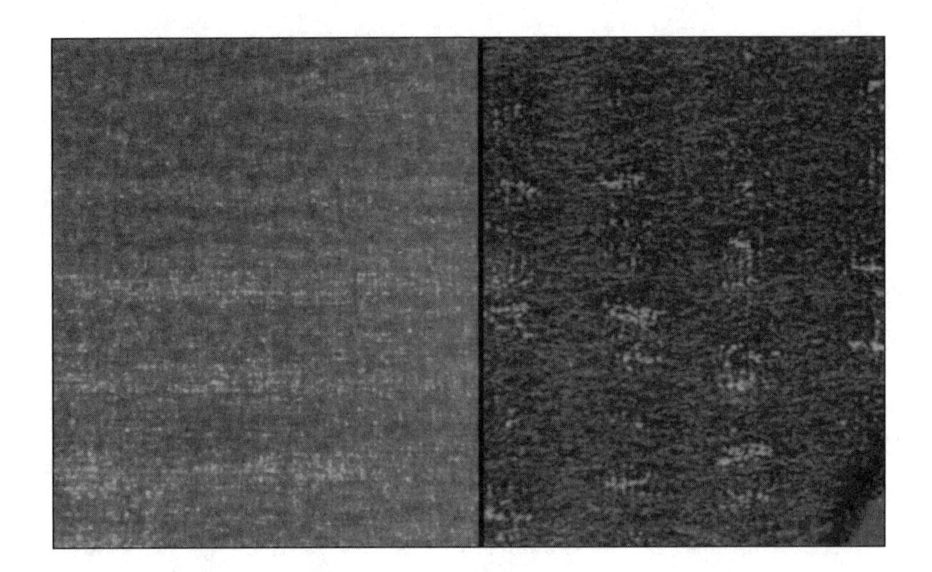

Causes	Remedies
Consistent variations in caliper of corrugated substrate corresponding with flute profile.	Improve corrugation process by reduced starch application and good liner selection to eliminate washboard at corrugator.
Incorrect plate impression.	Adjust plate to substrate impression.
Substrate surface finish resists ink wetting and lay.	Consult ink supplier for product or additive recommendations.
Ink film too thick for high hold-out substrates.	Reduce ink film thickness or use more porous substrate.
Ink film too thin for stock and the flute tip to flute valley caliper variation.	Improve corrugation process. Increase ink film thickness. Change ink formula for more transfer.
Ink viscosity too low.	Raise ink viscosity with fresh ink.
Ink formulation.	Consult ink supplier for recommendation.

Ink Foaming
(Flexo Presses Only)

Visible foaming in ink reservoir.

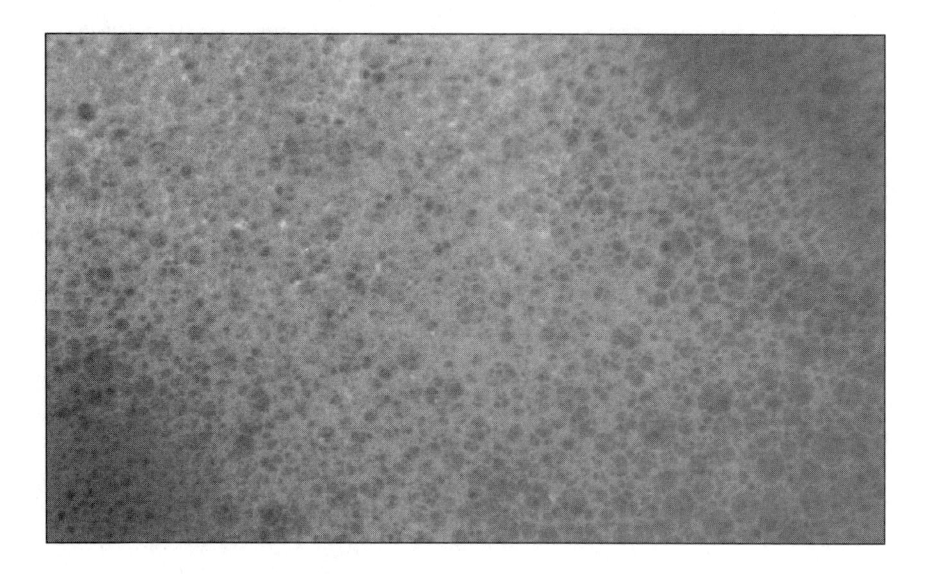

Causes	Remedies
Too much air being introduced into the ink.	Check for leaking pump seals or hoses on suction side and repair as required.
Excessive pump pressure causing splashing and aeration.	Reduce pump pressure(s) to minimum required (use pump **volume**, not pressure).
Excessive agitation of ink causing splashing and aeration.	Reduce pump or mixer speed to minimum required, keep ink return lines submerged.
Poor sealing of chambered doctor blade assembly.	Replace blades frequently. Adjust chamber for wipe and sealing. Adjust pumping to keep chamber full.
Too much water added to ink.	Raise ink viscosity with fresh ink.
Ink viscosity too high.	Lower viscosity to release trapped foam.
Ink formulation.	Add defoamer. Consult ink supplier for recommendation.

Pinholes or Fisheyes (Flexo Presses Only)

Frequently appearing spots on the printed surfaces.

Causes	Remedies
Excessive defoamer in or added to ink.	Replace ink or add fresh ink without defoamer. Consult ink supplier for recommendations.
Incompatible defoamer added to ink.	Replace ink or add fresh ink without defoamer. Consult ink supplier for product recommendations.
Surface tension of substrate too high.	Consult ink supplier for recommended products or additives for successful printing.
Excessive foam or micro foam in ink.	Eliminate foam or replace ink. See Ink Foaming on page 127 of this troubleshooting guide.

Dark or Dirty Print Color (Flexo Presses Only)

Printed color appears darker or dirty when compared to a color chip or other standard.

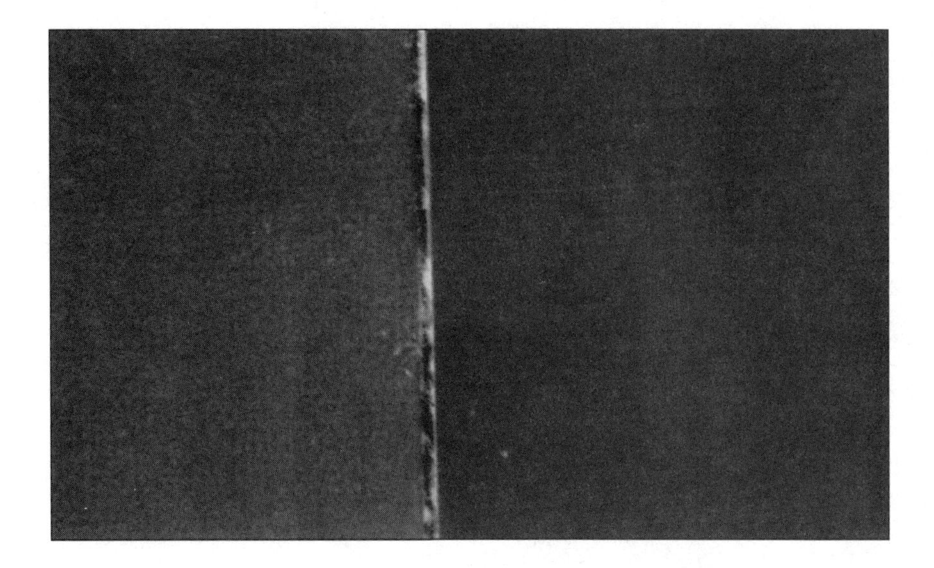

Causes	Remedies
Ink viscosity too high.	Lower ink viscosity.
Ink colorant (pigment) concentration too high for press or job configuration.	Add extender to ink. Reduce ink film thickness.
Ink film too thick for job.	Reduce ink film thickness by: Lowering ink viscosity. Increasing ink metering effectiveness. Changing ink formulation for less transfer. Decreasing machine speed. Decreasing anilox volume.
Ink contamination from prior color(s) not cleaned from press.	Thoroughly clean press station between color changes and replace ink.
Ink formulation.	Consult ink supplier for recommendation.

Mottled Print (Flexo Presses Only)

A speckled or "pebbled" condition.

Causes	Remedies
Inconsistent surface finish or caliper of substrate.	Increase plate to substrate impression. Increase ink viscosity. Increase ink film thickness. Use plates with softer durometer. Reformulate ink for substrate.
Incorrect plate impression.	Adjust plate to substrate impression.
Substrate surface finish or textured pattern on surface.	Replace stock and consult ink supplier for product or additive recommendations.
Ink viscosity too low.	Raise ink viscosity with fresh ink.
Too much water added to ink causing ink to be out of balance.	Add fresh ink or replace ink in press sump.
Dirty or camouflaged anilox roll.	Clean or replace anilox roll.
Contaminated ink in press.	Clean press station, replace ink.
Ink pH too low.	Check and adjust ink pH to specification.
Ink formulation.	Consult ink supplier for recommendation.

Uneven Print (Flexo Presses Only)

Printed color appears inconsistent in either machine or across machine direction.

Causes	Remedies
Ink metering system out of adjustment or damaged.	Check and adjust, repair or replace press components as necessary.
Across Press Variations:	
Light to dark from roll parallel.	Parallel all anilox/metering rolls/blades.
Streaks from grooved wipe roll.	Replace wipe roll.
Streaks from worn doctor blade.	Replace doctor blade.
Streaks from warped blade.	Reduce blade pressure or replace blade.
Streaks from damaged anilox roll.	Replace anilox roll.
Streaks from dirty anilox roll.	Clean anilox roll.
Streaks from low ink flow.	Increase ink flow through/across press.
Through Press Variations:	
Light to dark from low ink flow.	Increase ink flow through press.
Loose plates or plate mount.	Remount plates or mount to cylinder.
Roll bounce from gears, bearings.	Check and repair press as required.

Inconsistent Print Color (Flexo Presses Only)

Causes	Remedies
During Press Runs:	
Change in ink viscosity.	Monitor and control pH and viscosity.
Changes in substrate.	Control substrates, or adjust inks for stock.
Additions to ink in press.	Monitor, measure, and control all materials added to ink at press.
Between Different Press Runs:	
Changes in ink, substrate, run conditions, press configurations, suppliers, operator measurement or machine settings and speed.	Monitor, document, and then control critical variables of print process on each order to allow reproducible print performance by your plant and operators.
Between Different Press Stations:	
Differences in applied ink film thickness between print stations.	Adjust or formulate inks to correspond to various station configurations such as: Anilox volume, cell count, and condition. Metering type, pressures, and condition.
Changes in ink, substrate, press construction, plates, run speed or conditions, suppliers, operator measurement or machine settings.	Measure, document, and understand differences so that proper materials and procedures are used to minimize the effect of changes in your process.

Dirty Print/Dot Bridging (Flexo Presses Only)

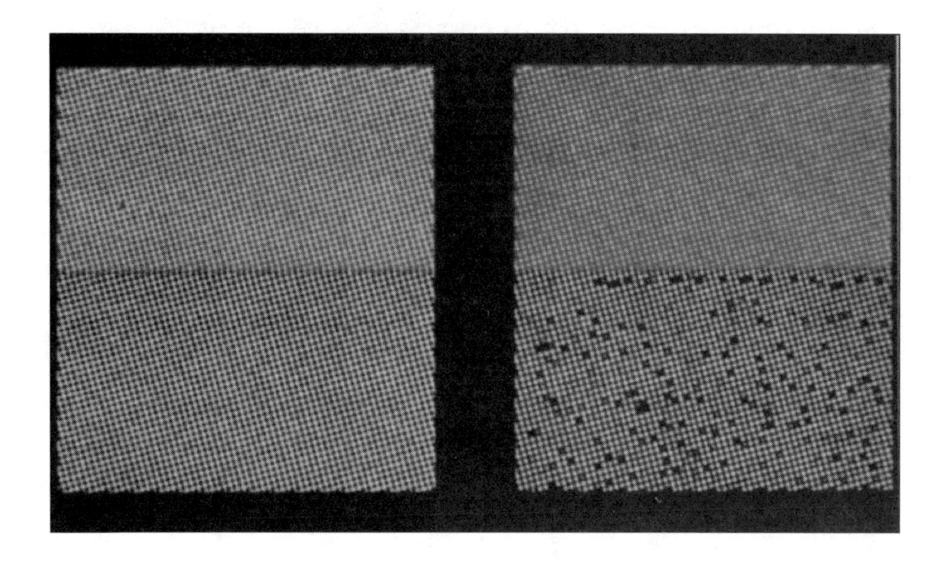

Causes	Remedies
Excessive plate impression.	Reduce plate to substrate impression.
Ink pH too low.	Check and adjust ink pH to specification.
Excessive anilox to plate pressure.	Adjust to reduce anilox impressions, check plate level.
Ink film too thick for plate screen.	Reduce ink film thickness by: Lowering ink viscosity. Increasing ink meeting effectiveness. Decreasing anilox volume.
Inadequate ratio of dot sizes (print screen) to anilox cell count.	Revise art, screens, and plates for press capabilities.
Ink drying too fast.	Slow drying by adding slow solvents. Eliminate air or heat blowing on plates. Increase machine speed.
Paper dust from stock or pressroom which collects in press or ink and sticks to plate.	Clean substrate prior to print stations, clean press, plates, and environment, ensure clean, sharp slitting and sheeting.
Uneven ink film applications due to machine or unlevel plates.	Adjust ink metering, print and anilox impressions, roll parallel, replace plates.
Printing plate too soft.	Use plates with a harder durometer.

Weak Print Color (Flexo Presses Only)

Printer color appears weak, faded, or light when compared to a color chip or other standard.

Causes	Remedies
Too much water added to ink from water left in press station or operator error.	Replace ink or add fresh ink. Repair station to drain washup water. Measure and control water addition to ink.
Worn or dirty anilox roll.	Clean or replace anilox roll as required.
Ink viscosity too low.	Raise ink viscosity by adding fresh ink.
Ink film thickness too thin.	Increase ink film thickness by: Raising ink viscosity. Reducing metering of anilox roll. Increase anilox roll volume. Changing ink formula for more transfer.
Incorrect plate impression.	Adjust plate to substrate impression.
Ink formula does not contain enough colorant for press or job configuration.	Consult ink supplier for ink formulas custom matched to your plant's product mix and press configurations.
Printing plate too hard.	Use plates with a softer durometer.
Plates glazed or dirty.	Clean or replace plates.
Substrate surface finish resists ink wetting.	Consult ink supplier for product or additive recommendations.
Ink formulation.	Consult ink supplier for recommendations.

Insufficient Ink (Flexo Presses Only)

Print image faded or non-existent.

No Photo Available

Causes	Remedies
No ink in reservoir	Replenish reservoir.
Air pressure lost	Find and correct trouble.
Electricity failure	Find and correct trouble.
Incorrect setting of circulating system valves	Check valve setting.
Ink foaming	Add defoamer to ink.
Ink spilled on floor	Put doctor blade assembly in position, or turn air pressure on.
Clogged hoses	Remove and clean.
Ink circulating system filter clogged	Remove and clean filter.
Ink return pump clogged with paper dust	Dismantle return pump and clean out (must be done once a week at last washup).
Pump not turned on	Ensure that system switches are activated; press reset button.
Pump jammed or malfunctioning	Check pump.

B. Sample Anilox Rolls

The anilox roll is the heart of all flexo folder gluers and rotary die cutters. There are three main types of anilox rolls used in flexographic printing. Mechanically engraved chrome plated rolls deliver excellent print quality, but are susceptible to wear and are easily damaged. Mechanically engraved ceramic rolls are more durable, but do not provide quality ink metering, and their abrasive surface can cause excess wear on the doctor blade or wiper roll. Laser engraved ceramic rolls, which are more expensive, offer durability and print quality, especially when used with a doctor blade system, and are the most commonly used rolls in the industry. A fourth type that is seldom used is a random cell roll. Ceramic coating is sprayed on the roll and forms the cells. It is very abrasive, and provides poor ink metering and print quality. This makes the roll unusable for today's graphic requirements.

The engraving on an anilox roll consists of cells of a specified design, theorectical volume, line screen count and angle. The primary function of the anilox roll is to transfer a thin uniform wet film thickness to a printing plate. The thickness is dependent on the cell volume, the uniformity is determined by screen count and cell angle. Surface geometry of a laser engraved ceramic roll with a 60–degree hexagon pattern is most desirable as it adds 15% more cells per inch, while reducing cell volume. Reduced cell volume provides a thinner ink film that yields higher fidelity graphics from more efficient ink release. It is also easier to clean.

The key for a printer is to select the highest line screen per lineal inch that yields the desired volume required to print the graphic. First, select the desired volume of ink that is required to give the proper color density for the job to be printed. Factors that need to be considered are ink chemistry, pigment percentage, doctoring system, and substrate on which the printing is being done. Second, choose the line screen count that is the highest possible that will still provide the required ink volume and remain in the specifications of an anilox supplier's range of volume for that screen count. An exception might be a printer who uses inks with high solids that might clog up the smaller cells. In that case, a lower screen count with larger cells would be advisable.

In today's corrugated industry, an average line screen count and volume, measured in billions per cubic micron, are approximately 200 cells per lineal inch at 8.5 BCM for printing on linerboard. The boxmakers need to base their anilox roll needs on plant and customer requirements and on future forecasted new business. The following illustrations show different syles of anilox rolls, noting deficiencies, strengths and applications:

1. Random cell rolls — Inconsistent print quality
2. Chrome rolls tool engraved — Good print— Very easily damaged short roll life.
3. Ceramic rolls tool engraved — Inconsistent volumes.
4. Ceramic rolls — Laser engraved rolls have good printing capability and good roll life.
5. Extreme caution should be taken when applying any type of non-skid application on a roll to roll / wiper blade system.

All plants should base their anilox rolls needs on plant and customer requirements and on future forecasted new business.

- Laser engraved ceramic rolls
- Tool engraved ceramic rolls (inconsistent volumes)
- Chrome rolls. Excellent print quality / short roll life.

For process printing, laser engraved rolls with wiper blades will give you the best quality.

Sample Anilox Rolls

(Continued)

The following pages include photo-micrographs of anilox cell shapes and cell counts with specifications as to the particular configuration and surface coatings. We do not make recommendations as to which anilox roll cell count to use on a particular type of printing requirement. It is recommended that the anilox roll manufacturer be called in for a consultation prior to the selection of any anilox cell count or for a particular graphics requirement.

NOTE:

- Rolls numbered 800, 600, 400 and 200 are general references.
- Rolls numbered 01 through 05 are specific examples of anilox rolls.
- Rolls numbered 06 through 14 show examples of various types of wear or damage.

Anilox Roll References

(BCM = Billion Cubic Microns)

Roll Number:	800
Line Screen:	800
Angle:	60°
Cell Depth:	8.0
Opening:	28.8
Wall:	3.0
Bottom:	0.0
Est. Volume:	1.9 BCM

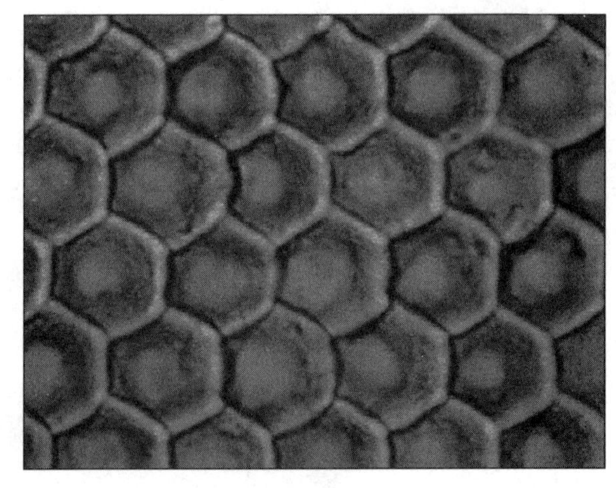

400 X.

Roll Number:	600
Line Screen:	600
Angle:	60°
Cell Depth:	13.0
Opening:	38.3
Wall:	4.0
Bottom:	0.0
Est. Volume:	3.0 BCM

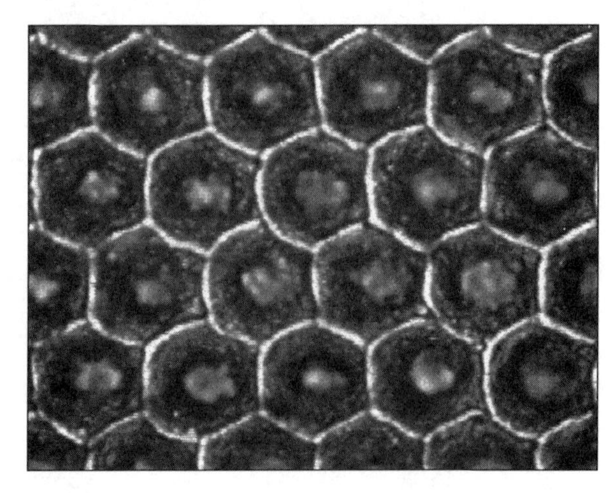

400 X.

NOTE: These two anilox roll examples with 600 and 800 line cell counts would only be recommended for use on pre-printing liner board when used in conjunction with 120 line or higher printing plate screen values. They are not normally used when post printing sheets of corrugated board.

Sample Anilox Rolls

Roll Number:	400
Line Screen:	400
Angle:	60°
Cell Depth:	17.0
Opening:	58.5
Wall:	5.0
Bottom:	0.0
Est. Volume:	4.3 BCM

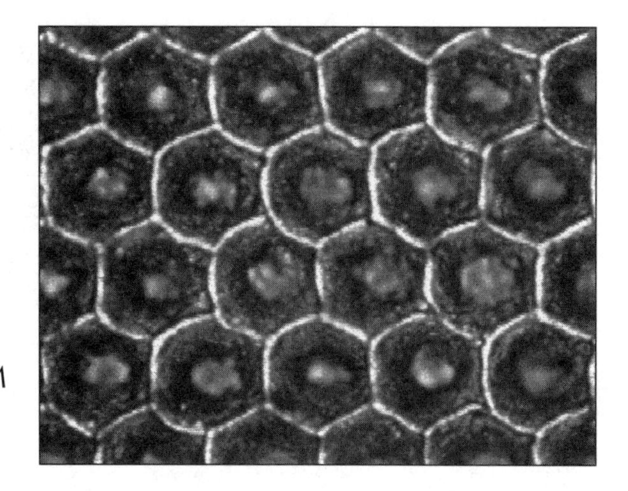

200 X.

Roll Number:	200
Line Screen:	200
Angle:	60°
Cell Depth:	34.0
Opening:	120.0
Wall:	7.0
Bottom:	0.0
Est. Volume:	7.0 BCM

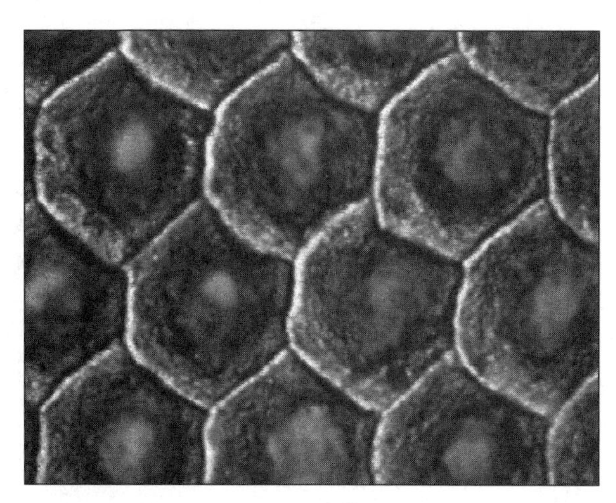

200 X.

NOTE: Roll number 200 with 200 line cell count is typical of anilox rolls in many general purpose direct printing corrugated flexo presses. Roll number 400 with 400 line cell count would be recommended only for process printing of graphics where printing plate screen values of 100 to 120 line screen values are used. The use of this low volume anilox cell would apply a very thin ink film and may not be suitable for heavy solids and some line copy. It is recommended that consultation with the anilox roll manufacturer be made prior to the use of this fine line anilox cell count roll.

Sample Anilox Rolls

Roll Number:	01
Line Screen:	260
Angle:	45°
Cell Depth:	34.0
Opening:	84.7
Wall:	13.0
Bottom:	20.0
Calculated Volume:	7.1 BCM

100X magnification. Mechanical chrome-plated engraving. Chrome thickness typically = .0005"
Linescreen range: 11–550 cells/inch. Volume range:100–2.5 BCM.
Excellent release characteristics. Short life span due to wear/damage.
Clean with a brass bristle brush.

Chrome plated anilox rolls provide smooth ink transfer and are in high demand by many industries using flexographic printing. A care and maintenance program which includes daily cleaning of the printing station and brushing of the anilox roll must be implemented when using chrome plated rolls in order to obtain maximum longevity.

Roll Number:	02
Line Screen:	135
Angle:	45°
Cell Depth:	40.0
Opening:	151.1
Wall:	37.0
Bottom:	70.0
Calculated Volume:	9.3 BCM

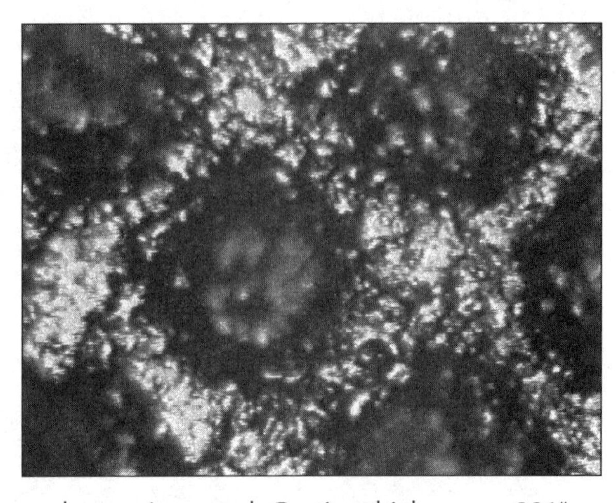

100X magnification.Mechanically engraved ceramic-coated. Coating thickness = .001".
Linescreen range: 11–300 cells/inch. Volume range: 90–2.2 BCM.
Less efficient than chrome-plated engraving because of texture of ceramic coating.
Line screen volume limitations. Clean with a steel bristle brush.

Sample Anilox Rolls

Roll Number:	03
Line Screen:	240
Angle:	30°
Depth:	37.0
Opening:	87.8
Wall:	18.0
Bottom:	0.0
Calculated Volume:	7.4 BCM

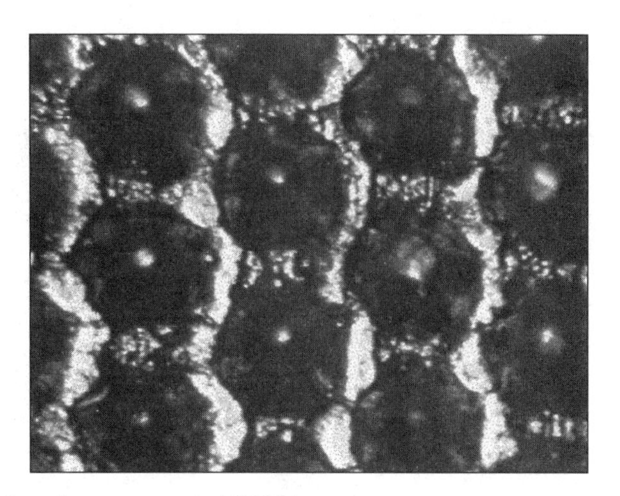

100X magnification. Laser engraved 30° Hex.
Linescreen range: 100–600 cells/inch. Volume range: 3–20 BCM.
Not as geometrically sound as 60°Hex. Generally used for coating application.
Wide/irregular walls.

Roll Number:	04
Line Screen:	300
Angle:	45°
Cell Depth:	34.0
Opening:	68.7
Wall:	16.0
Bottom:	20.0
Calculated Volume:	6.6 BCM

100X magnification. Laser-engraved 45° Diamond/Quad.
Linescreen range: 85–800 cells/inch. Volume range: 2–40 BCM.
Wide walls and post areas. High recast tips, rough surface texture. Channeling due to irregular recast build-up.

Sample Anilox Rolls

Roll Number:	05
Line Screen:	500
Angle:	60º
Cell Depth:	13.0
Opening:	46.8
Wall:	4.0
Bottom:	0.0
Calculated Volume:	3.2 BCM

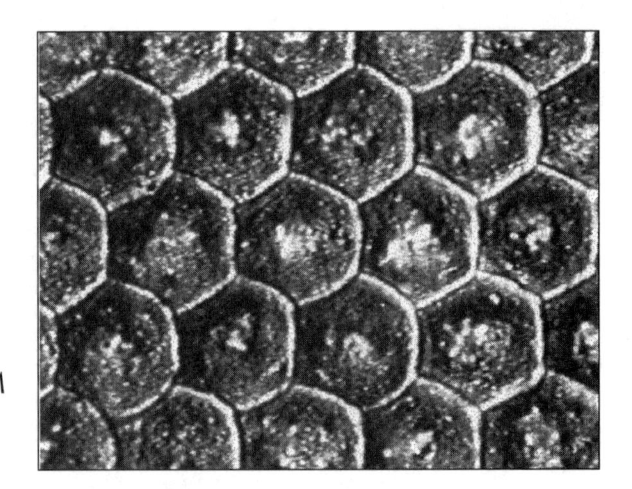

200X magnification. Laser engraved 60º Hex.
Linescreen range: 100–1200 cells/inch. Volume range: 1.0–21 BCM.
Engraving within proper depth-to-opening ratio.
Engraving characterized by thin, smooth cell walls and excellent geometric cell structure.
Engraving is efficient, easy to clean, and reproducible.

Roll Number:	06
Line Screen:	500
Angle:	60º
Cell Depth:	6.0
Opening:	47.8
Wall:	3.0
Bottom:	0.0
Calculated Volume:	1.5 BCM

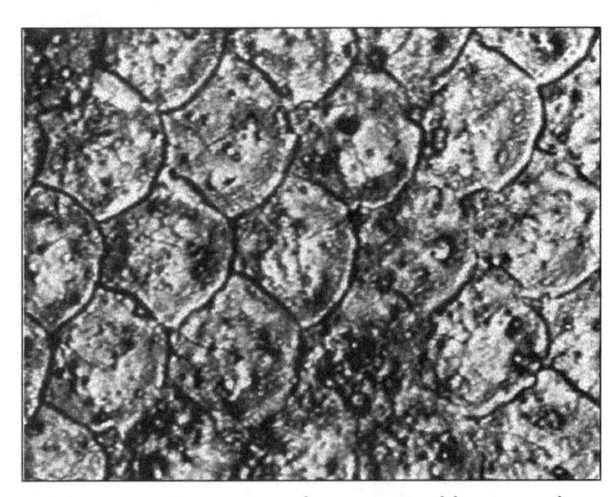

Poor cell geometry. Depth-to-opening ratio = 13%. Engraving characterized by irregular cell walls, misformed or missing cells and poor geometric quality. Expect inconsistent ink delivery, excessive blade and or plate wear, and short roll life.
Engraving impossible to reproduce accurately.

NOTE: Anixlox rolls with 500 cell count are only recommended for printing fine line copy and process printing using printing plates with screen values of 120 and under. They are not generally used when printing solids and heavy line copy.

Sample Anilox Rolls

Roll Number:	07
Line Screen:	500
Angle:	60°
Cell Depth:	21.0
Opening:	43.8
Wall:	7.0
Bottom:	0.0
Calculated Volume:	4.5 BCM

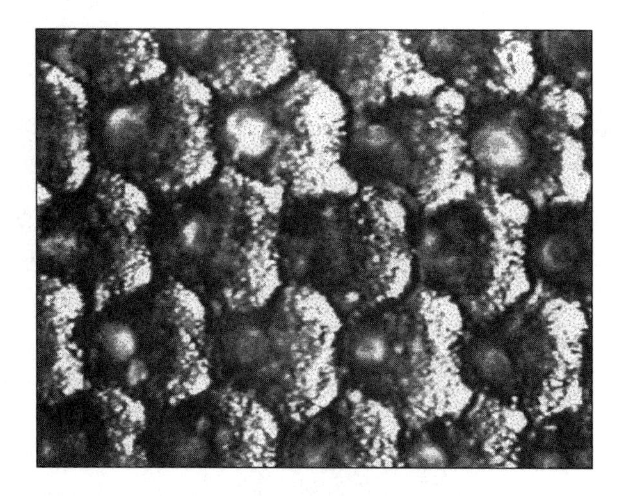

Poor cell geometry. Depth-to-opening ration = 45%. Engraving characterized by high recast tips/rough surface texture, wide walls, and channeling due to irregular recast build-up. Monitor for excessive blade or plate wear due to rough surface texture. Monitor for pinholes and/or striations. Expect excessive plugging/difficulty cleaning. Engraving impossible to reproduce.

Roll Number:	08
Line Screen:	0
Angle:	NA
Cell Depth:	0.0
Opening:	0.0
Wall:	0.0
Bottom:	0.0
Calculated Volume:	0.0

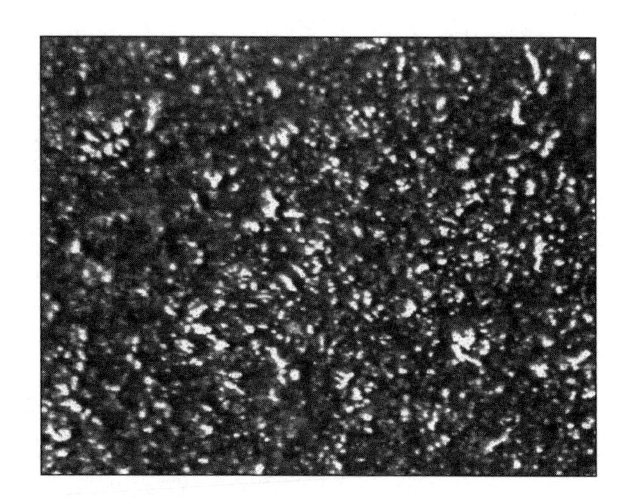

Ceramic as sprayed.
Textured/Smooth ceramic, although not used for high quality graphic reproduction. Finds applications in the transfer of adhesives and other materials that do not require controlled metering. Clean with a steel bristle brush.

Sample Anilox Rolls

Roll Number:	09
Line Screen:	260
Angle:	60º
Cell Depth:	32.0
Opening:	80.7
Wall:	17.0
Bottom:	0.0
Calculated Volume:	6.4 BCM

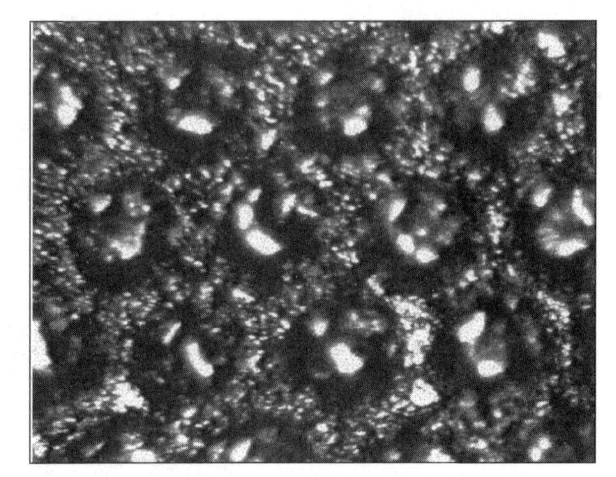

Ultrasonic exposure. Damaged or missing walls. Channeling due to damaged or missing walls. Rough surface texture. Poor ink transfer, print coverage. Suggest replacement.

Roll Number:	10
Line Screen:	0
Angle:	NA
Cell Depth:	0.0
Opening:	0.0
Wall:	0.0
Bottom:	0.0
Calculated Volume:	0.0

Ultrasonic damage. Damaged/missing areas, poor ink transfer, print coverage.

Sample Anilox Rolls

Roll Number:	11
Line Screen:	440
Angle:	60º
Cell Depth:	12.0
Opening:	40.7
Wall:	17.0
Bottom:	0.0
Calculated Volume:	1.7 BCM

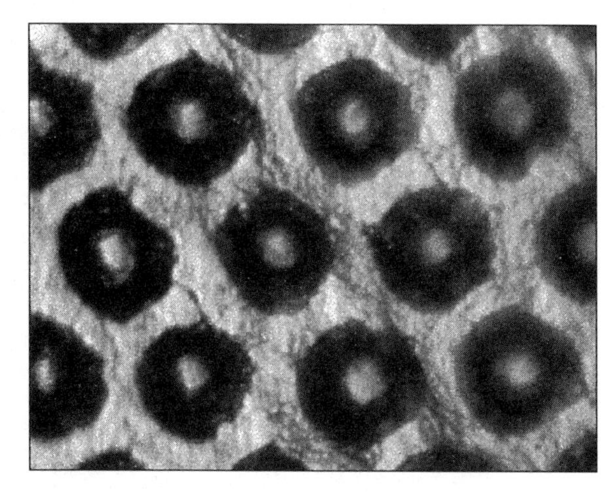

200X magnification. Laser engraved 60º Hex showing extreme wear, poor ink transfer, print coverage.

Roll Number:	12
Line Screen:	440
Angle:	60º
Cell Depth:	16.0
Opening:	50.7
Wall:	7.0
Bottom:	0.0
Calculated Volume:	3.6 BCM

Excessive use of sodium bicarbonate exposure/damage. Poor ink transfer, print coverage.

Roll Number:	13
Line Screen:	280
Angle:	60°
Cell Depth:	24.0
Opening:	82.7
Wall:	8.0
Bottom:	0.0
Calculated Volume:	5.3 BCM

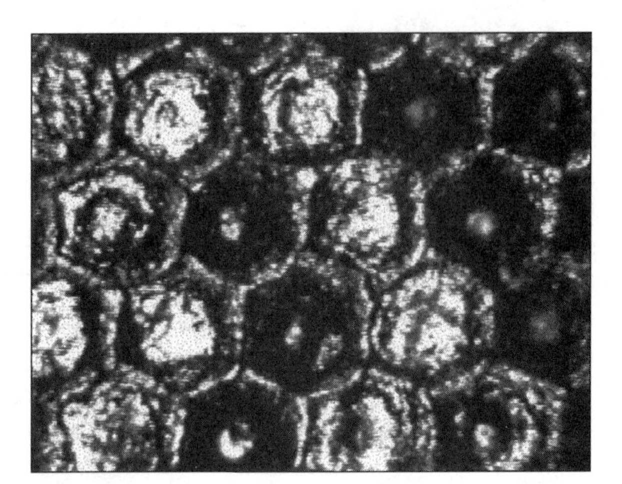

100X magnification. Acceptable engraving. Cells heavily plugged; clean roll thoroughly. Continue to use.

Roll Number:	14
Line Screen:	280
Angle:	60°
Cell Depth:	24.0
Opening:	82.7
Wall:	8.0
Bottom:	0.0
Calculated Volume:	5.3 BCM

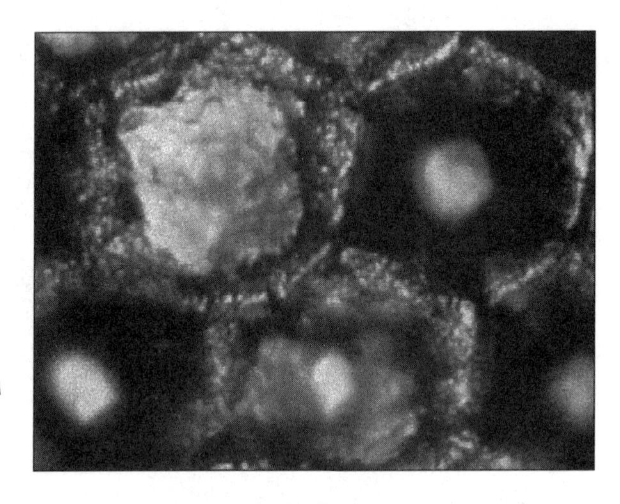

200 X magnification. Clean cell vs. Plugged cells. Clean roll thoroughly. Continue to use.

Summary: Sample Anilox Rolls

Roll Number	L/S	Angle	Cell Depth	Opening	Wall	Bottom	Cell Volume	Comments / Recommendations
01	260	45°	34.0	84.7	13.0	20.0	7.1	100 X Magnification. Mechanical chrome-plated engraving. Chrome typically =.0005". Linescreen range: 11–550 cell/inch. Volume range: 100–2.5 BCM. Excellent release characteristics. Short life span due to wear/damage. Clean with a brass bristle brush.
02	135	45°	40.0	151.1	37.0	70.0	9.3	100 X Magnification. Mechanically engraved ceramic-coated. Coating thickness =.001". Linescreen range: 11–300 cells/inch. Volume range: 90–2.2 BCM. Less efficient than chrome-plated engraving because of texture of ceramic coating. Line screen volume limitations. Clean with a steel bristle brush.
03	240	30°	37.0	87.8	18.0	7.4		100 X. Laser engraved 30° Hex. Linescreen range: 100–600 cells/inch. Volume range: 3–20 BCM. Not as geometrical sound as 60°Hex. Generally used for coating applications. Wide/irregular walls.
04	300	45°	34.0	68.7	16.0	20.0	6.6	100 X Magnification. Laser-engraved 45° Diamond/Quad. Linescreen range: 85–800 cells/inch. Volume range: 2–40 BCM. Wide walls and post areas. High recast tips, rough surface texture. Channeling due to irregular recast build-up.
05	500	60°	13.0	46.8	4.0	0.0	3.2	200 X Magnification. Laser engraved 60°Hex. Linescreen range: 100–1200 cells/inch. Volume range: 1.0–21 BCM. Engraving within proper depth-to-opening ration. Engraving characterized by thin, smooth cell walls and excellent geometric cell structure. Engraving is efficient, easy to clean, and reproducible.
06	500	60°	6.0	47.8	3.0	0.0	1.5	Poor cell geometric. Depth-to-opening ratio = 13%. Engraving characterized by irregular cell walls, misformed or missing cells and poor geometric quality. Expect inconsistent ink delivery, excessive blade and or plate wear, and short roll life. Engraving impossible to reproduce accurately.
								*BCM = Billions of Cubic Microns

Summary: Sample Anilox Rolls

Roll Number	L/S	Angle	Cell Depth	Opening	Wall	Bottom	Cell Volume	Comments / Recommendations
07	500	60°	21.0	43.8	7.0	0.0	4.5	Poor cell geometry. Depth-to-opening ratio = 45%. Engraving characterized by high recast tips/rough surface texture, wide walls and channeling due to irregular recast build-up. Monitor for excessive blade or plate wear due to rough surface texture. Monitor for pinholes and/or striations. Expect excessive plugging/difficulty cleaning. Engraving impossible to reproduce.
08	0	NA	0.0	0.0	0	0.0	0.0	Ceramic as spayed. Textured/Smooth ceramic, although not used for high quality graphics. Finds applications in the transfer of adhesives and other materials that do not require controlled metering. Clean with a steel bristle brush.
09	260	60°	32.0	80.7	17.0	0..0	6.4	Ultrasonic exposure. Damaged or missing walls. Channeling due to damaged or missing walls. Rough surface texture. Poor ink transfer, print coverage. Suggest replacement.
10	0	NA	0.0	0.0	0.0	0.0	0.0	Ultrasonic damage. Damaged/missing areas. Poor ink transfer, print coverage.
11	440	60°	12.0	40.7	17.0	0.0	1.7	200 X Magnification. Laser engraved 60° Hex showing extreme wear. Poor ink transfer, print coverage.
12	440	60°	16.0	50.7	7.0		3.6	Sodium bicarbonate exposure/damage. Poor ink transfer, print coverage.
13	280	60°	24.0	82.7	8.0	0.0	5.3	100 X Magnification. Acceptable engraving. Cells heavily plugged; clean roll thoroughly. Continue to use.
14	280	60°	24.0	82.7	8.0	0.0	5.3	200 X Magnification. Clean cell vs. Plugged cells. Clean roll thouroughly. Continue to use.

*BCM = Billions of Cubic Microns

Part 3: Die Cutting Problems

Flat Bed, Platen and Rotary Die Cutting Defects

In order to correctly build cutting dies, it is important to know the type of diecutting machine on which the dies will be used. It is also important to distinguish between the terms flatbed and platen type diecutter. This following section pertains to flatbed diecutters and soft anvil rotary diecutters, with some reference to platen type diecutters.

A flatbed diecutter has a reciprocating bed (the flatbed) onto which a flat die is secured. A hardened steel cylinder acts as the cutting anvil while the cutting die travels underneath, cutting through the material from below. This type of diecutter is known as a reciprocating flatbed cylinder press. A Miehle would be representative of this type of die cutter.

The platen type diecutter utilizes a flat die between two bolsters, one of which is mobile and presses the material against the cutting and creasing rules of the die. A Bobst would be typical of this type of die cutter.

The simplest version platen press is the jaw or clam-shell type press. The more automated platen presses have a gripper bar / board conveying system with a mobile platen operating from the bottom up or from the top down.

Rotary soft anvil diecutters utilize a rotary cutting die (shaped to fit around a die drum). This type of die cuts against a rotary soft anvil cylinder and both top or bottom rotary diecutters exist.

Good diemakers are not developed overnight and with the advent of rotary die cutting and automatic stripping on platen die cutters higher quality dies than ever before are required. Inadequate fitting of rules results in uncut "nicks" which makes waste difficult to separate from finished blanks. All joints should be butt joints and where it is not possible to make butt joints, such as in "T" intersections, the rule should be carefully fitted to match the bevel at the cutting edge. In some cases the performance of the die can be improved by spot welding.

Biased Blanks (Flat Bed)

Blank becomes biased after square infeed.

Causes

Feed or transfer shafts are worn or misaligned; one or more mechanical transfer and gripper components fail blank contact or are worn to prevent proper transport timing.

Remedies

Check for wear on feed and transfer shafts and replace if necessary.
Correct any misalignment.
Position grippers correctly or replace if worn.

Inaccurate Crease

Inaccurate crease or cut lines from accurate dies.

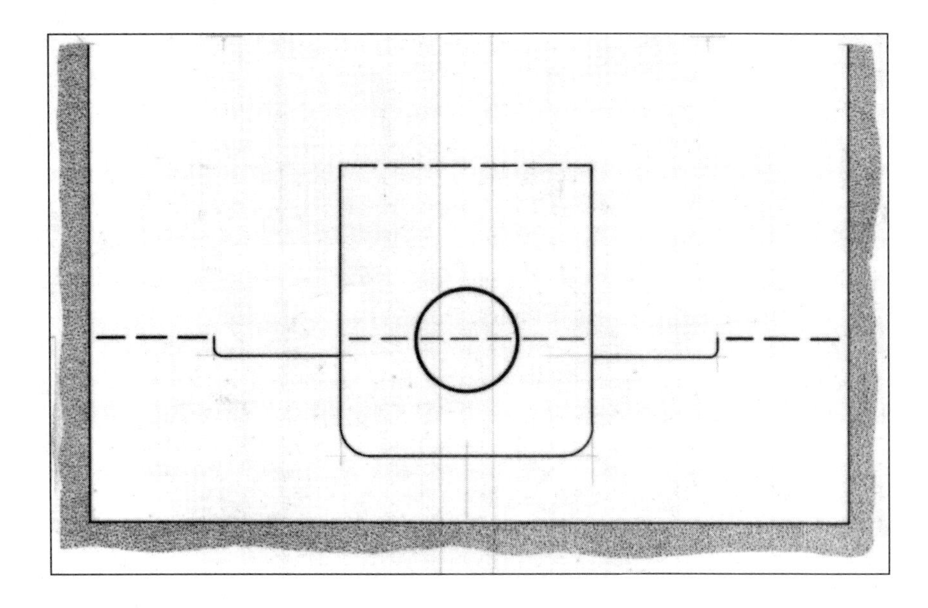

Causes	Remedies
Rule too high in die board which may be too thin, allowing die deflection.	Adjust height of rule and check die holder.
Rule too thin and deflecting.	Use thicker cutting rule.
Inadequate support for the rule.	Notch the rule and drive a corrugated fastener in the board where the rule is notched. Consider the use of surface mounted scoring rule with crushing area built in to the rule (as done in Rotary).
Rubber too close to rule.	Set rubber out (1/16'') from rule.
Scoring rule is too high or too narrow.	Adjust height of score.
Rubber too close to scoring rule.	Rubber away from scoring rule. Do not rubber scores on flat dies.

Fracture At Crease (Flat Bed, Rotary, or Platen)

Paper creases fracture.

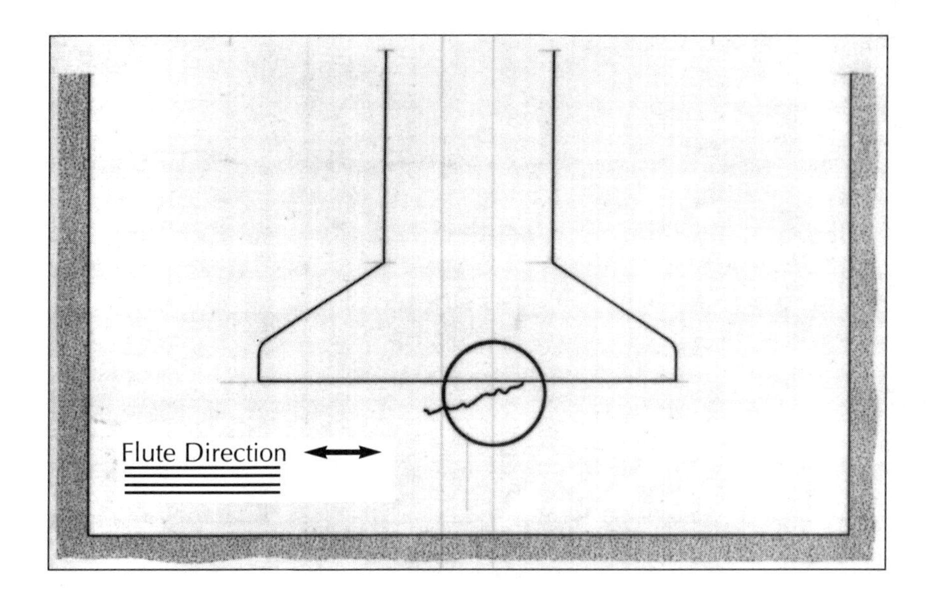

Causes	Remedies
Creasing rule too narrow for dry board, causing fiber breakage instead of bending.	Humidify board if practicable, or, go to thicker scoring rule. Consider surface mounted creasing rule with crushing shoulders built in (Rotary).
Burr develops in knife from pulling operation during repairs.	File down burrs each time a rule is pulled. Use proper knife puller.
Ineffective or improper rubbering along score lines.	Replace with firm rubber.
Scoring rule too narrow or too high.	Should use 4 pt., 6 pt., or 8 pt. score.
Bent, crushed or damaged rule.	Replace rule.

Board Sticks To Die (Flat Bed)

Board does not eject after die cutting.

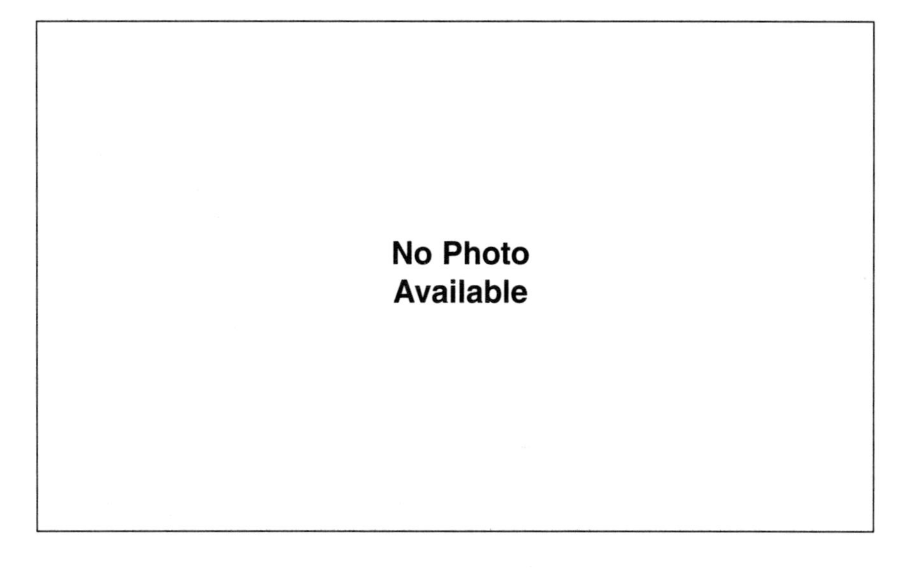

Causes	Remedies
Insufficient leaf springs and open area ejection rubber on die.	Provide additional leaf spring capacity.
Insufficient, improperly placed, or improper type of ejection rubber (Rotary).	Place current type of ejection rubber in the correct locations.
Poor rubbering techniques.	Eliminate parallel sides, finish product with ejection rubber.

Hanging Trim (Flat Bed, Rotary, or Platen)

Slotted cuts or leading edge trim hangs on die.

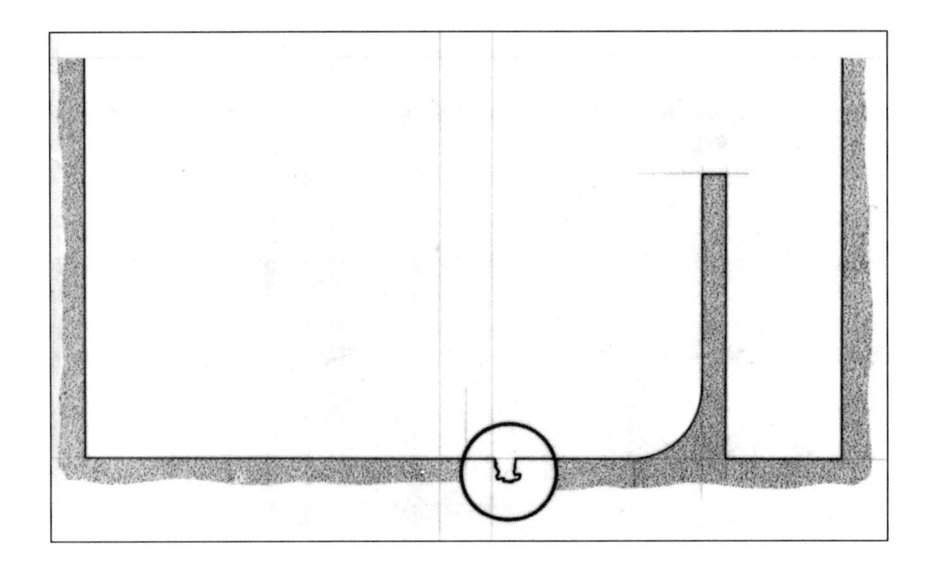

Causes	Remedies
Nicking in die to retain paper attachments is burred.	Remove burr at nicking points of die. Use a grinder to make nicks; do not use a chisel.
Bent, crushed, or damaged rule.	Re-rule.
Insufficient amount of ejection rubber (Rotary).	Add ejection rubber.
Improper joint construction between two segments of cutting rule.	Solder joints. Re-rule. Join or miter properly. Use silver solder at joints.
Insufficient amount or type of stripping rubber.	Add stripping rubber or replace with correct rubber.

Cutout or Trim Not Stripping (Flatbed or Rotary)

Large trim does not fall free after cutting.

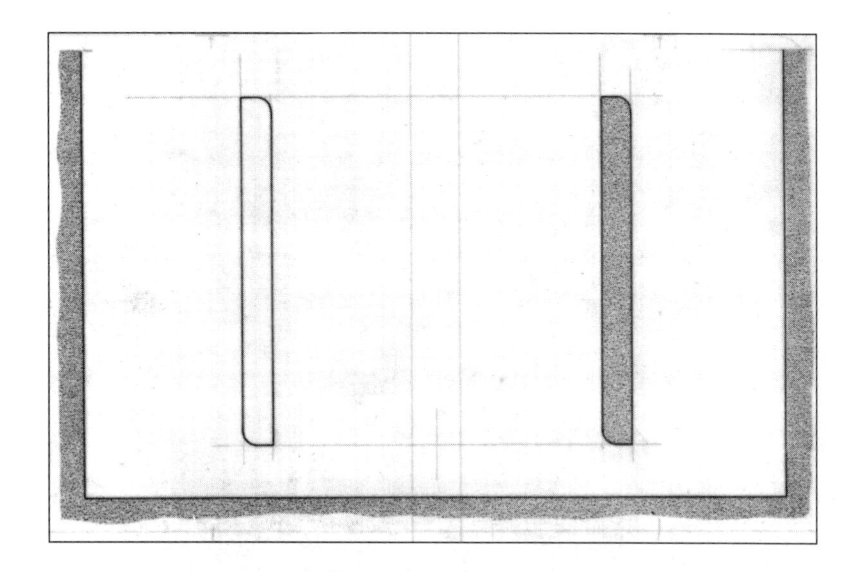

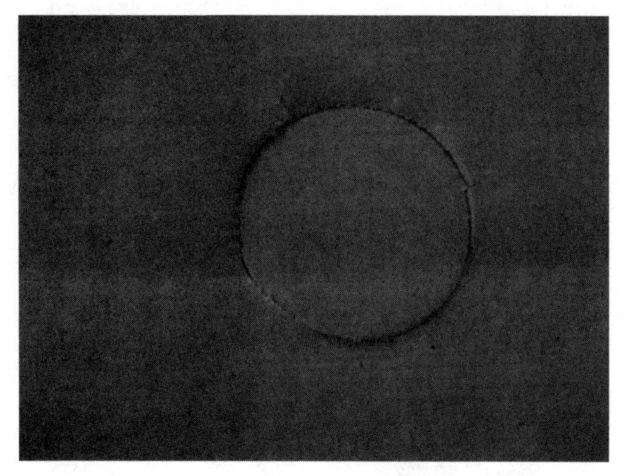

Causes	Remedies
Insufficient rule extensions into trim area.	Replace with longer rules.
Rule too thin.	Increase rule thickness.
Improper stripping rubber.	Check and provide proper stripping rubber (type, size and location).
Insufficient number of trim breaker or chopper knives.	Add trim breaker knives or chopper knives.
Incomplete cutting.	See "Die Not Cutting", page 158–159.
Nick holding scrap to blank.	Reknife die to eliminate rule joints. Redesign blank to eliminate rule joints.
Improper blank design.	Redesign blank. Bend all corners. Eliminate parallel sides in feed direction with diagonal choppers.

Ragged Edge
(Flat Bed)

Paperboard rips in grippers (Flat Bed) or in die when leaving die cutting operation.

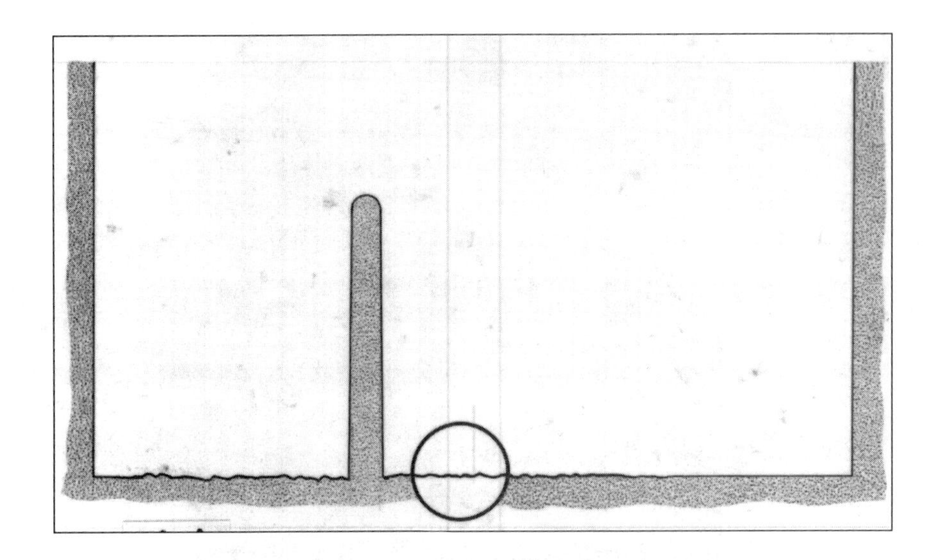

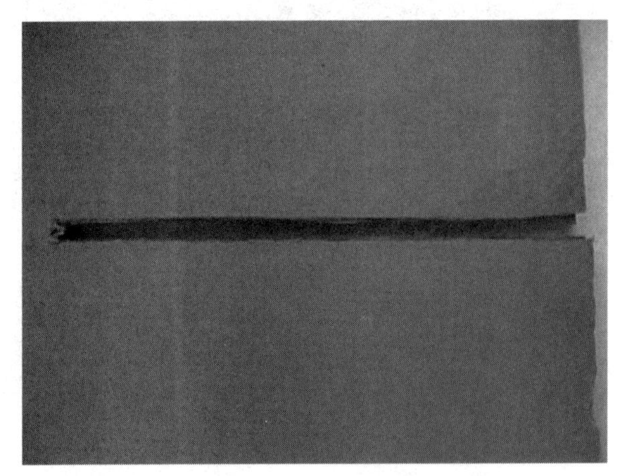

Causes	Remedies
Inadequate ejection rubber leaves paper hung in small holes and corners after gripper transit begins (Flat Bed).	Rebuild die with adequate ejection rubber.
Burrs on cutting rule nicks.	Remove burrs from nicks or replace rule. Make nicks with a grinder, not a chisel.
Insufficient gripper bite on board (Flat Bed).	Increase gripper bite.
Worn out ejection rubber.	Replace the rubber and make sure that high quality rubber of the right durometer is used for replacement.
Dull worn rule.	Re-rule cutting rule.
Inadequate makeready.	Increase makeready.
Inadequate impression setting.	Increase tonnage.

Sticking Slots (Flat Bed and Rotary)

Slots not stripping.

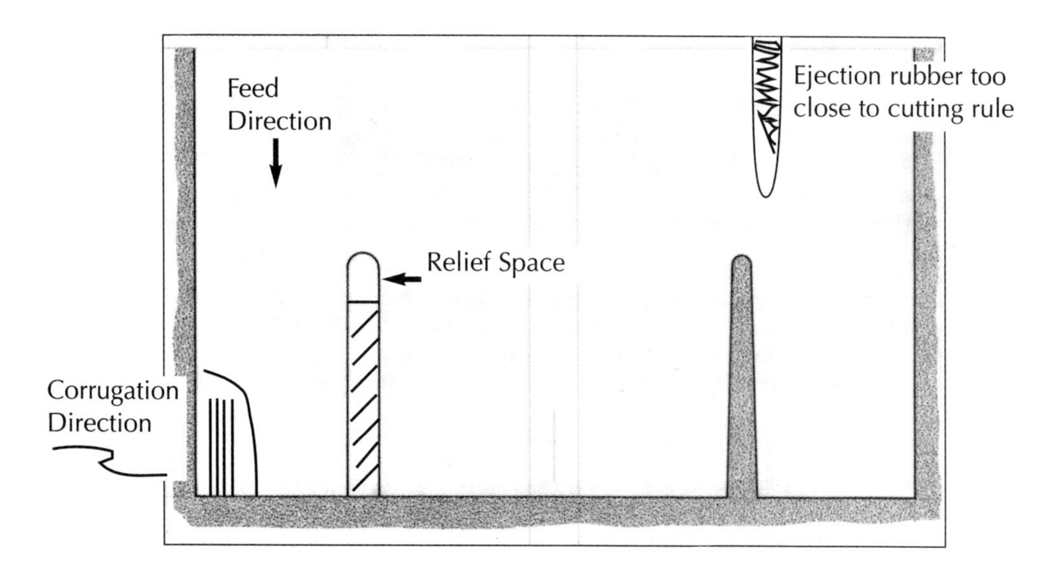

Causes	**Remedies**
Slots improperly shaped.	Taper slots. Consider slits instead of slots.
Inadequate stripping rubber.	Add correct amount of stripping rubber.
Improper rubbering techniques.	Follow slot rubbering techniques.
Ends of slots rubbered without relief.	Rubber slots with proper relief as shown in picture.
Product ejection rubber too close to slots (Rotary).	Keep product ejection rubber 1 1/2" away from slots.

Die Not Cutting (Flatbed, Rotary, and Platen)

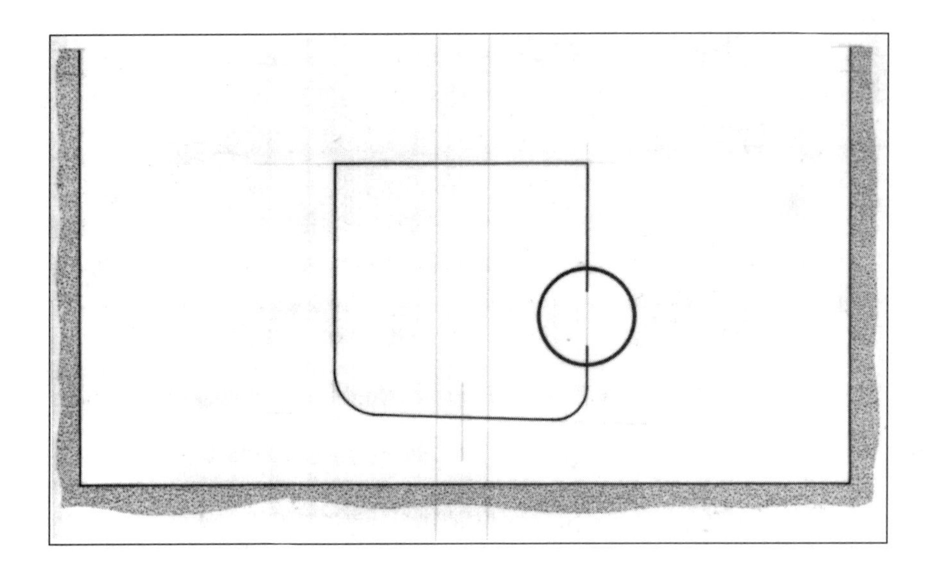

Condition 1

Frequent but intermittent loss of full depth impression.

Causes	Remedies
Excess make-ready sheets are permitting spongy die movement (Flat Bed).	Remove excessive make-ready sheets.
Unevenly worn anvil blanket (Rotary).	Rotate blankets. Replace blankets. Trim blankets.

Condition 2

Blanks consistently uncut in one area.

Causes	Remedies
Die is not flat on chase; chase is not locked; make-ready sheet and die are off center to chase bearers or not padded correctly (Flat Bed).	Check for flatness of die and die backing; secure chase if not locked; correct die for centering; correct rule height if not parallel with chase; more make-ready in uncut area.
Improper score height for liners of board being die cut.	Use correct score height. Too high score prevents proper penetration of cutting knives.
Machine out of alignment. (Flat Bed)	Balance both sides.
Improper make-ready due to sharing of cutting die between platen proofs. (Flat Bed)	This is an improper practice and should not be done.

Die Not Cutting

(Continued)

Condition 3

General (Rotary)

Causes	Remedies
Stripping rubber too near cutting die rule.	Provide sufficient space between stripping rubber and cutting rule.
Damaged cutting rule edge.	Repair or replace rule.
Poorly made joint.	Reinforce joint, replace rule to eliminate joint, or, if between score rule and cutting rule, relieve score rule at joint with the cutting rule.
Worn anvils.	Replace anvils.

Condition 4

Intermittent cut (Rotary)

Causes	Remedies
Lower shaft deflecting for large linear inch cut.	Reduce linear length of rule. (For example: going from a 4–out to a 2–out, minimum blank size permitting).
Worn anvils.	Replace anvils.
Poorly made joint.	Reinforce joint. Replace rule to eliminate joint. If joint is between scoring and cutting rule, relieve scoring rule at joint with the cutting rule.
Too much stripping rubber, improper rubber location.	Re-rubber die using proper height, hardness type (cell type) and location of rubber.

Improper Impressions (Rotary)

Dies fail to strip.

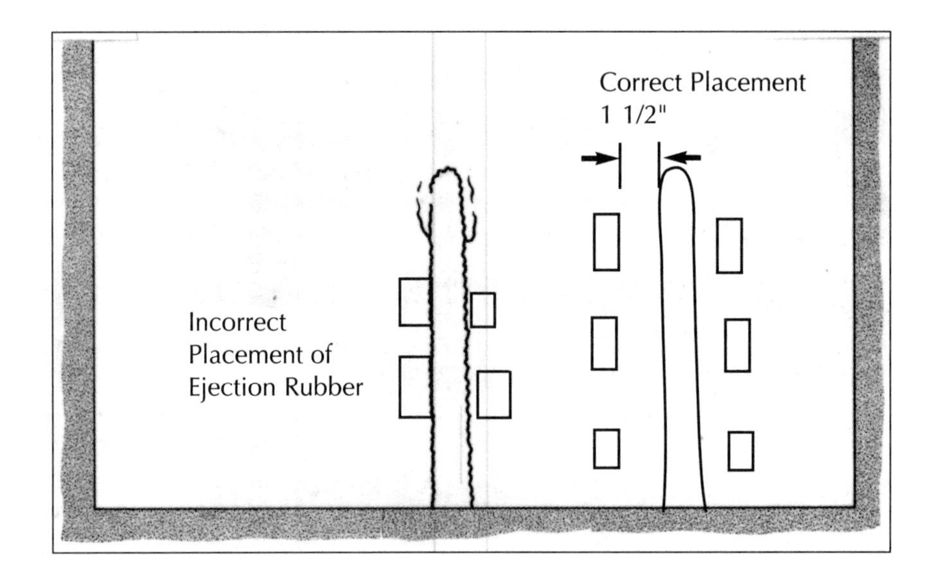

Causes	Remedies
Deep impressions ruptures rubber; rubber adhesion lost or incorrect height. Too much rubber.	Reduce rubber impression. Repair rubber strippers for adhesiveness or height.
Die not bolted down properly.	Ensure that all bolt holes are used to secure die to cylinder.
Burrs in knife.	Grind or file off burrs.
Slots too narrow.	Increase slot width.
Ejection rubber too close to stripping area.	Move ejection rubber 1 1/2" from cutouts.

Decreasing Die Cut (Rotary)

Dies gradually stop cutting.

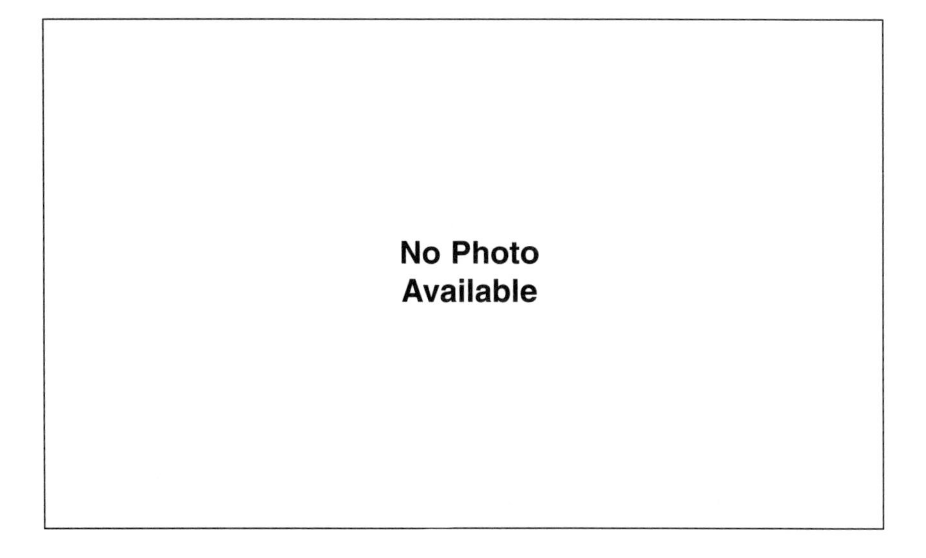

Causes	Remedies
Worn blankets.	Replace worn anvils.
Oscillation problem.	Check for proper anvil oscillation.

Uncut Corners

Corners and holes not cut through.

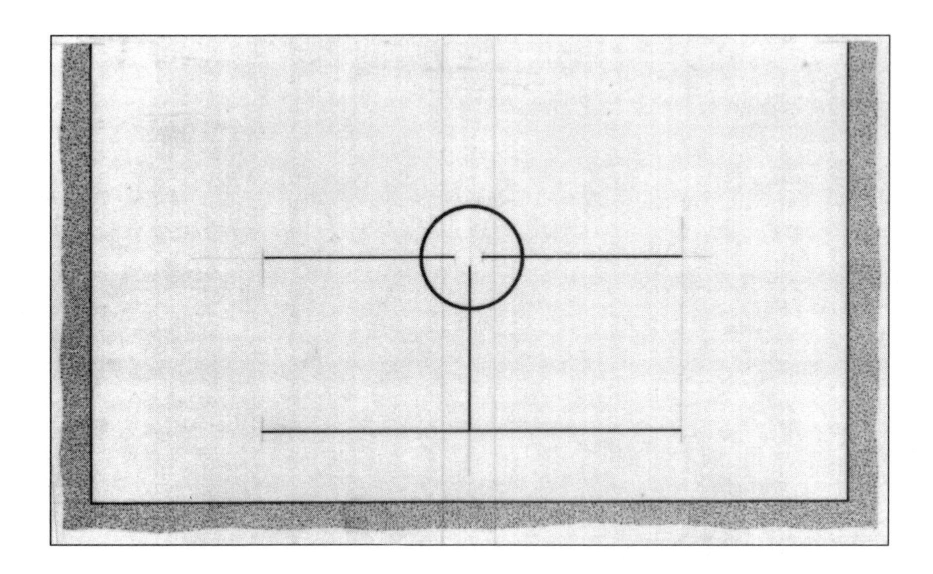

Causes	Remedies
Too much stripping rubber if make-ready sheet test as proper cut (Flat bed).	Reduce height and/or width of stripping rubber.
Cutting rules not properly fitted together.	Fit the rules together to prevent accumulation of paper fiber in the crevice, which will spread the rules apart.
Rubber too close to rule.	Set rubber out from rule.

Uneven Cutting
(Rotary)

Deeper cut on one side of machine.

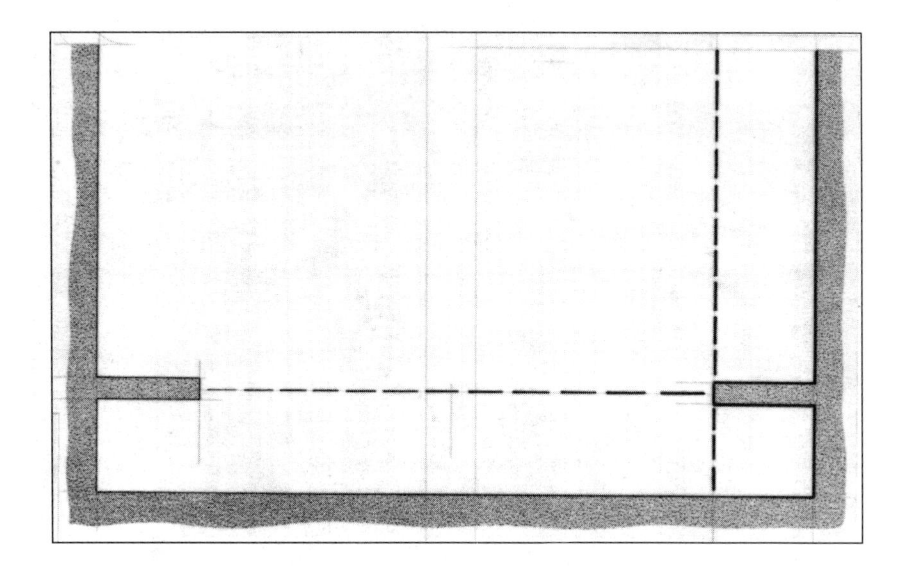

Causes	Remedies
Shafts not parallel or not aligned with machine.	Align and parallel the shafts.
Die not bolted correctly or missing bolts.	Bolt die to cylinder correctly. Repair cylinder holes if damaged.
Mistake in die.	Correct mistake.
Worn blanket.	Replace blanket.

Breaking Dies
(Rotary)

Dies fracture at start.

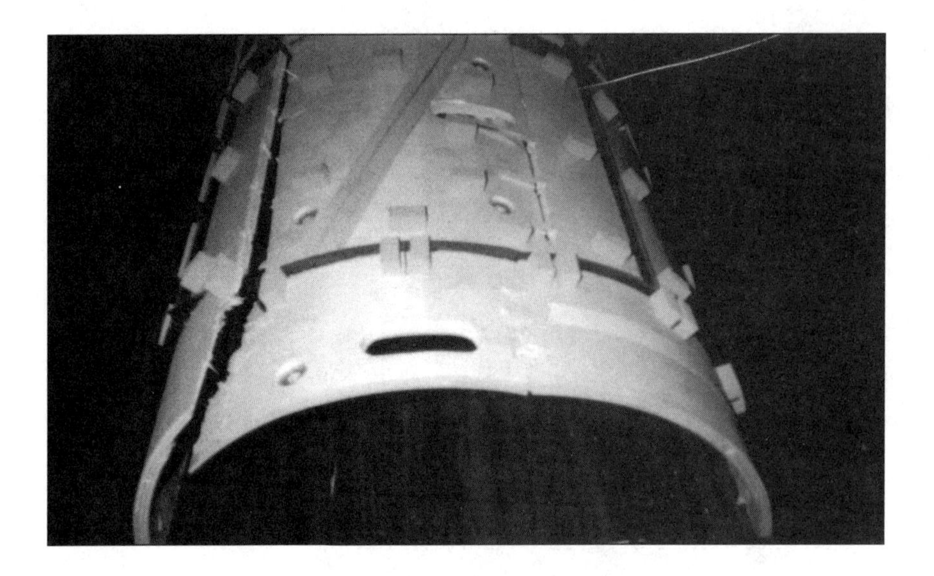

Causes	Remedies
Incorrect anvil line-up.	Correct anvil line-up.
Die not bolted down properly.	Use all bolt holes to secure die to cylinder.
Latch strip not seated properly.	Seat latch strip properly.
Scores sticking up out of die.	Seat scores with mallet.
Excessive makeready under die.	Remove makeready.

Deflection Problems
(Rotary)

Dies will not cut different test boards on other orders.

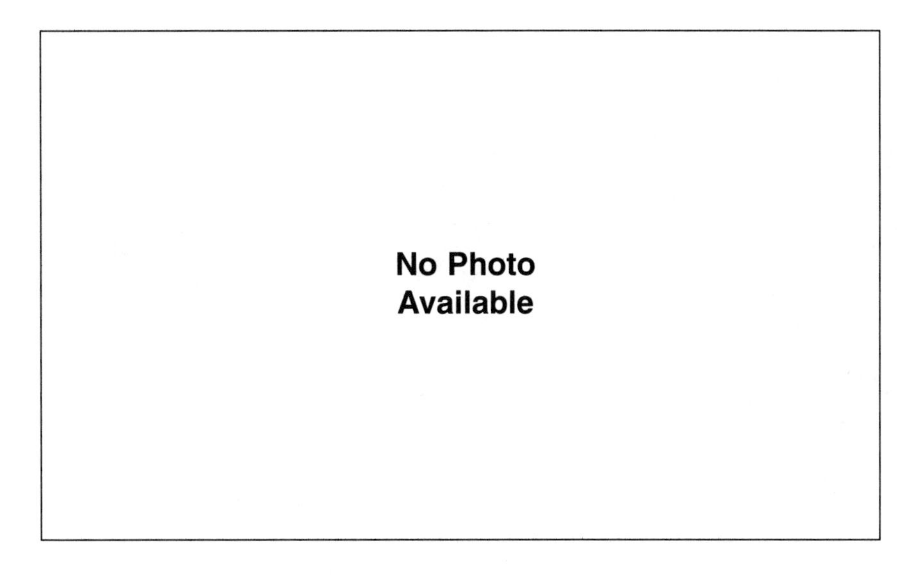

Causes	Remedies
Anvil shaft deflections vary with test and shims are insufficient for heavier board.	Reduce lineal length of rule die. Replace anvils.
Incorrect cutting rule height.	Use correct height rule.
Wrong die design.	Build correctly (knife and score heights).
Wrong impression setting.	Check impression (see horizontal score from printed side of diecut).

Crushed Board
(Rotary)

Board crushed during and after die cutting.

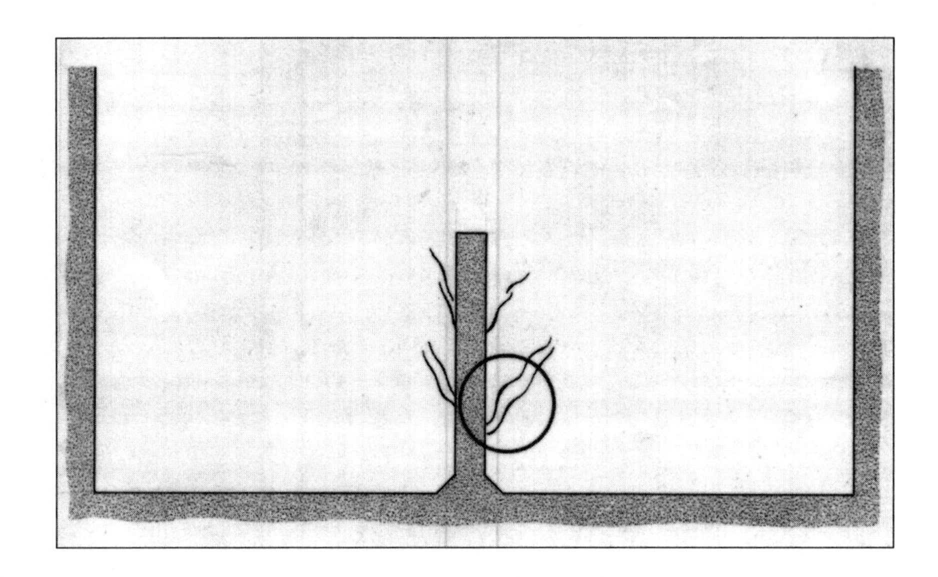

Causes	Remedies
Feed roll too tight (Rotary)	Open feed roll gap but take care that loss of sheet contrtol does not result
Inadequate clearance for stripping rubber; also, light basis weight or dried out paper.	Reduce height of stripping rubber and/or width. Humidify board if practicable. Use lower durometer rubber.
Improper placements of stripping rubber (Rotary)	Slot rubber should be high density, closed cell. All slot rubber should have 1/16" clearance on the sides. Lead edge: Trail portion of slot should have 3/16" clearance to allow for displacement (see Example 1). Trail edge: Lead portion of slot should be tight against the closed end of the slot (see Example 2).

Example 1

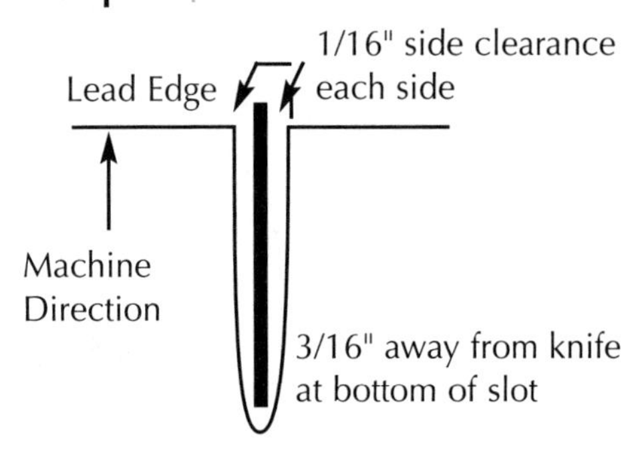

Example 2

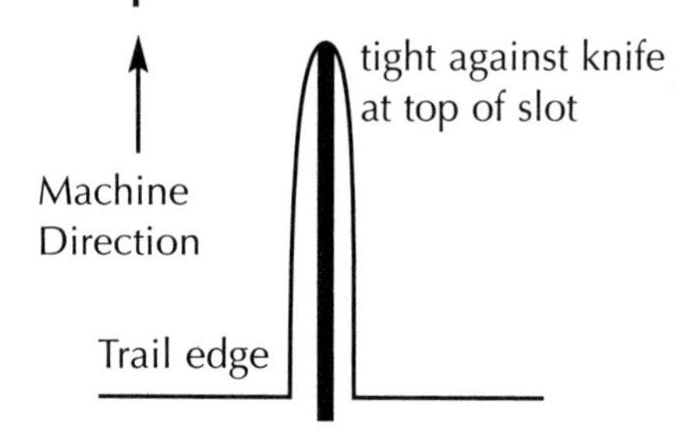

Improper Die Register (Flatbed and Rotary)

Blanks missing correct cut register or register on bias.

Note dimension difference between the "P" in "POPS" and the edge of the corrugated diecut and the "N" in "POPCORN" and the edge of the corrugated diecut.

Causes	Remedies
Transfer belt speeds varying with one another or register stop out/position or time. (Flat bed).	Check and correct transfer belt speeds register and timing.
Kicker is not locked parallel or chase incorrectly located. (Flat bed).	Make kicker parallel and check for correct location of chase.
One or more bent gripper bars. (Flat bed).	Replace bars.
Die cut cylinder out of time with rest of machine (Rotary).	Adjust running register to bring cutting die cylinder into time with rest of machine.
Slippage of blank between printing station(s) and die cutting section (Rotary).	Check pull collar shaft(s) and printing cylinder/impression cylinder gaps. Adjust nip points for proper grip of sheet through the press. Add pull bands to print station(s). Add pull collars.
Slippage in die cut station (Rotary) caused by uneven anvil blanket wear and/or improper gap slitting (Rotary).	Rotate anvil blankets. Replace anvil blankets. Adjust cutting cylinder/anvil cylinder gap to eliminate slippage. Add pull band rubber to cutting die.
Insufficient rubbering in cutting die (Rotary).	Add stripper rubber for improved sheet control.

Loss of Dimensional Stability (Rotary)

Excessive sheet length variation.

No Photo Available

Causes	Remedies
Lack of pull rubber	Check pull rubber.
Over or under penetration of rule	Check cutting impression.
Uneven anvils	Rotate anvils more frequently.
Scoring rule height too low or too high	Rerule die with proper height score rule.
Register problems	See "Improper Die Register" page167.
Excessive rubber	Remove unnecessary rubber.

Abnormal Anvil Wear (Rotary Only)

Premature, excessive, or localized wear in the die cutter anvils.

No Photo Available

Causes	Remedies
Too much penetration between die and anvil drum	Check impression setting.
Anvil drum not oscillating	Check panel light and oscillating mechanism.
Improper cover rotation	See TIP 0305-35.
Damaged cutting rule	Repair or replace damaged rule.
Improper rule height	Correct rule height.
Improper anvil rotation schedule	Consult supplier for proper anvil rotation schedule.
Dieboard too thick; rule too short	Use correct wood thickness.
Not enough room for paper and rubber	Use correct height to give more room. Use correct rubber height.

Excessive Makeready Time (Platen)

Abnormally long makeready.

No Photo Necessary

Causes	Remedies
Bent, worn or broken platen drive components preventing flat seating of die onto paper—usually accompanied by excessive internal noise and time to "spot up" one side or make-ready sheets.	Check drive components of machine and repair as required.
Heavy paper grades (TW,DW).	May be impractical to run.
Crews insufficiently and improperly trained.	Crews require adequate and proper training.
Too many ups and outs (also too many inches of rule)	Decrease number of ups or/and outs.
No balance knives	Use balance knives.

NOTE: Platen die cutters tend to have unique "footprint". Therefore cutting dies should not be shared between presses. Set up time increases when fine-tuning an existing cutting die to a different platen die cutter.

Part 4: Finishing And Manufacturer's Joint Problems

A. Feed Section Problems
B. Slotting Section Problems
C. Folding Section Problems
D. Counter Ejection Section Problems
E. Glue Lap Problems
F. Stitching Problems
G. Taping Problems
H. Common Curtain Coating Problems

A. Feed Section Problems

Problem	Causes	Remedies
Sheets do not feed	Warp	Bend flaps if safe.
	Feed gate too tight	Check clearance with sample sheet from order and adjust.
	Kicker set improperly	Check setting against sheet size and adjust.
	Kicker not engaging	Remove tape, if used, on kicker blade and check wear of blade; replace if necessary.
	Hopper backstop set too tightly.	Check setting against sheet size and adjust.
	Too many sheets in hopper; sheets slipping	Reduce quantity in hopper.
	Moist sheets	Check order for moisture content. Remove to dry if necessary.
	Excessive speed for sheets	Reduce speed and/or quantity of blanks in hopper.
	Poor trim at corrugator causing crushing	Reduce speed; report defect to corrugator operator.
	Sheets too heavy for kicker blade springs	Reduce quantity in hopper and/or use sponge under blades.
	Lack of warp bar assist	Use a warp bar under the feed gates.
Double feeding of sheets	Feed gate(s) set too high	Reset gate to allow only one sheet through comfortably.
	Kicker blade too high	Add tape to kicker blade.
	Incorrect kicker bar	Use proper kicker bar for flute or order.
Sheets crushed	Feed roll set too tightly	Check setting and adjust.
	Crushed at the corrugator	Check caliper of sheets as received from corrugator.
	Feed rolls out of parallel	Check and adjust.
Sheets slipping	Worn feed roll	Check diameter of feed roll to see that it is uniform across machine; replace if necessary.
	Feed roll set too loosely	Check feed roll setting for sheets on current order and adjust.
	Slippery sheets	Check for wax offset, contaminated liner, and cleanliness of feed roll.
	Old feed roll	Check feed roll to see if it has hardened and has become too smooth (over 40 Shore A) to grip sheet firmly without crushing. Replace if necessary.
	Small blanks	Determine if blank dimension through machine is not below machine minimum.
	Excessive warp	Inspect and bend flaps if possible without loss of quality; if impossible, do not use.

B. Slotting Section Problems

Problem	Causes	Remedies
Incorrect panel sizes	Panel sizes improperly set	Adjust panel sizes.
	Panel size pointers moved or installed improperly	Check installation of pointers; move pointers if necessary to correct condition.
	Worn or missing wear shoes	Replace.
Jam-up	Point of upper stripper below bottom of upper slotter head	Adjust.
Slotter head marks on box adjacent to crease	Slotter head gap too tight	Adjust slotter for correct board caliper.
Lower slotting head plugged-up with slot trim	Eccentric lock screw loose	Tighten screw.
	Lower clearer/stripper not cleaning out slot trim; clearer worn or not adjusted properly	Install new clearer/stripper; adjust clearer/stripper setting.
Blanks not traveling from slotting section into folding rails properly	Upper stripper missing, causing blanks to rise; upper stripper too short, causing blank to catch on stripper	Install new upper stripper; adjust location of stripper.
Torn liner on crushed part adjacent to score lines	Old urethane scoring counterparts have become brittle and hard	Change urethane counterparts.
Scores out of center compared to slot or vice-versa	Improper alignment, faulty indexing	Correct alignment; check index fingers if out of place.
Lead flaps bend or tear	Dull slotting blades or misadjusted flap hold-downs	Check flap hold-downs (strippers); check slotting blades.
Glue tab extension folds over	Air jet blowing too hard	Adjust air if necessary; relocate or adjust direction of air blast.
Slots out of square compared to score lines	Pull shaft and slotting shaft clearance incorrect; badly worn slotting blades on one side of box	Set shaft clearance; check slotting blades; readjust lap cutting.
Sheet misalignment	Sheet slipping in previous sections	Check previous sections' troubleshooting sheets
	Losing sheet between scoring and slotting	Check incoming and outgoing pull collars for proper spacing and pressure; both must be on sheet
	One or more urethane covers on "female" heads worn excessively	Check condition wear of urethane pull collars covers; replace scoring head covers.
Losing sheets in pull collars between scoring and slotting	Sheet slipped in pull collars	Increase pull collar pressure to compensate for previous section pull collars, glue tab, and end crush; previous section pull collars may be too tight.

Slitting—Ragged

Refers to ragged cutting of the edges of a sheet and trim left attached.

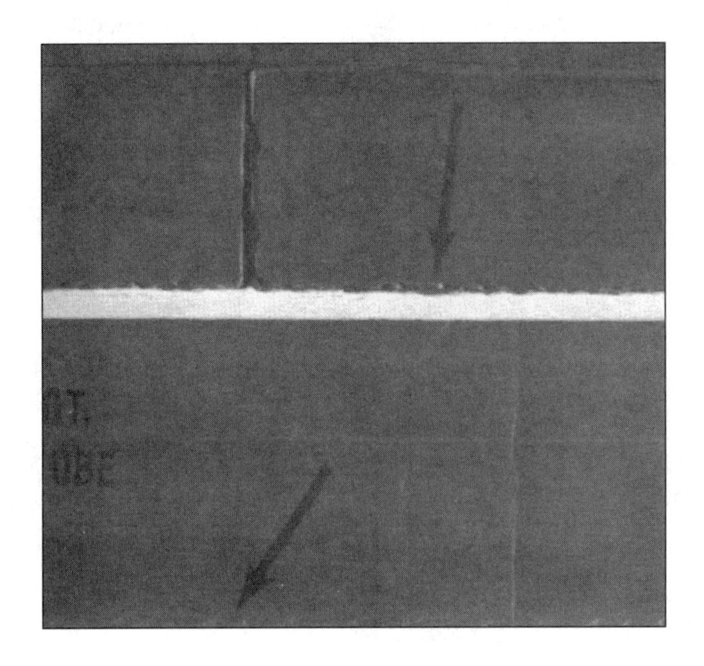

Causes	**Remedies**
Slitter head loose on shaft.	Tighten head.
Trim knives dull or worn.	Replace knives.
Trim knives not in contact.	Adjust trim knives to overlap.
Shafts out of line.	Parallel shafts.
Insufficient trim allowance.	Adjust Feed hopper side guides to provide proper trim allowance.
Combined board too wet, liners too wet.	Pull off job and allow board to dry. Advise corrugator departments to take corrective action on future orders.

Scoring Defects–Rolling Scores

Panel scores not folding uniformly or not folding at the proper location.

Causes	Remedies
Uneven break along scoring scoreline(s).	Reduce score head clearance. Replace worn creaser.
Slotter head gap too tight crushing blank too heavily redefining a wide area on which the fold could occur.	Adjust slotter head gap to minimize crush while still maintaining sheet control.
Scores weak despite apparent full penetration of male profile into anvil.	Scoring ring diameter too large therefore reducing scoring head shoulder crush. Replace scoring rings with proper diameter.

Scoring Defects—Panel Scores Cut or Rolling

Refers to the depth and character of all panel scores in the container Liner(s) cracked or checked along inside or outside of scoreline.

Causes	Remedies
Male-female scoring heads not aligned.	Align male and female scoring heads.
Insufficient clearance between male and female scoring heads.	Increase score head clearance.
Damage to scoring anvil or scoring profile.	Check for excessive wear or damage to scoring anvil or score profile. Replace as necessary.
Scoring heads or shafts are out-of-round.	Check for out-of-round on scoring heads or scoring shaft. Replace as necessary.
Linerboard problems.	Substrates (liners) are an increasing cause of score cracking. The three conditions below are difficult to overcome. Reducing preheater wraps on the corrugator and processing quickly following corrugating can reduce the problem. (1) Shorter fibers in recycled liners are more prone to drying on the corrugator and score cracking. (2) Wet end pressing on paper machines strengthens interfiber paper bonds and can cause cracking. (3) During the winter season, cold outside air, when warmed up to box factory ambient temperatures, becomes very dry and these dry conditions can promote score cracking.

Scoring Defects—Panel Scores Cut or Rolling

(Continued)

Causes

Liner/web overheated crystallizing anilox causing board to be brittle.

Remedies

Pre-crush scored area using pull collars or extra height pull bands on a non-printing cylinder (if possible and if box compression is not an issue.
Re-run order if score cracking is severe.
Advise corrugator crews to take corrective action on future orders.

Slots—Deep or Shallow

Refers to slots extending beyond flap scores into body of container, or slots not reaching to center of flap scores.

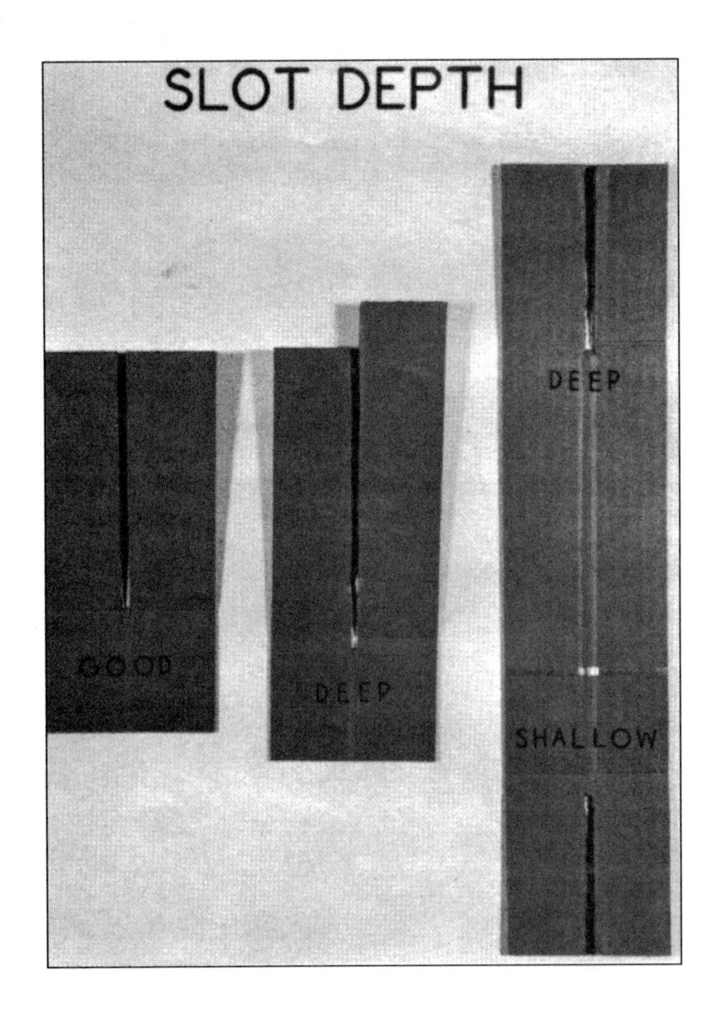

Causes	Remedies
Slots on slotter head incorrectly set.	Reset slots.
Excessive play in the gear train or keyways of the printing press causing properly set slot depths to oscillate with one becoming shallow and the opposite side becoming deep.	Perform maintenance on the gear train or keyways.
Warped stock causing infeed variation.	Bend flaps. Slow machine speed. Discard warped stock, re-corrugate any resulting shortage.

Slotting—Ragged

Refers to ragged cutting of slots and trim left in slots.

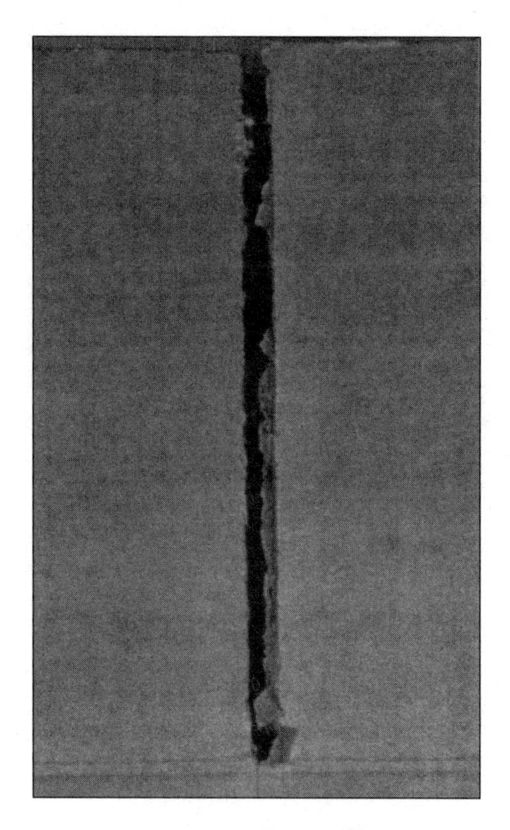

Causes	Remedies
Knife or blade dull.	Replace knives and blades.
Insufficient running interference between slotting knives and lower blades.	Tighten knives and blades.
Worn strippers.	Replace worn strippers.
Knife blade re-sharpened causing the blades to become under-sized.	Replace slotter knife blades with new ones at correct thickness.
Excessive adhesive applicator yielding wet combined board/wet board.	Allow board to dry out. Advise corrugator crews to take corrective action on future orders.
Lower slotter head not centered properly.	Adjust.
Box slipping in slotting position.	Readjust slotter head caliper setting.
Slotter heads improperly set for board caliper.	Readjust heads for caliper of board being run.

C. Folding Section Problems

Folding Section Jam Ups

No Photo Available

Condition 1

	Causes	Remedies
Jamming at entrance of folder	Missing or broken slot stripper	Replace as necessary.
	Excessive warp	Break flaps and reduce machine speed.
	Improper nip setting of folding rails	Adjust to proper nip.
	Worn lower folding belts	Replace as necessary.
	Lower belt support rollers stopping or flattened	Clean paper dust and replace as necessary.
	Incorrect board caliper adjustment	Set caliper for board being run.

Condition 2

	Causes	Remedies
Jamming at delivery end of folder	Loss of control of blank at delivery end	Adjust hold-down device to maintain proper control.
	Excessively warped blanks	Break flaps and reduce machine speed.
	Too tight or too loose transfer mechanism	Adjust for proper position.
	Incorrect board caliper adjustment	Set caliper of board being run.
	Folding section out of line	Check machine alignment.
	Skewed sheet	Refer to all Causes/Remedies in Conditions 1 and 2.

Conveyor Belt Damage to Box

Refers to crushing of box panel opposite manufacturer's joint and can also cause false scores and a "5-panel" box when it is set up by the customer.

Causes	Remedies
Excessive conveyor belt pressure on taping machine.	Adjust conveyor belt pressure to obtain minimum taping pressure damage and proper tape application.
Excess pressure at "spin off" rolls on folder-gluer sections where boxes are discharged into accumulating hopper section.	Reduce pressure (open gap) at "spin off" rolls consistent with maintaining proper blank control.
Insufficient pressure on "crushing" collars used to crush tab and edge of fourth panel, creating excess thickness at the manufacturer's joint. Discharge pressure conveyors "emboss" the excess caliper into the area opposite the manufacturer's joint causing a false score.	Adjust "crushing" collars to achieve desired crush without creating a false score.

Pull Collar and/or Feed Roll Damage—Excessive

Refers to pull collars and/or feed rolls crushing the board over .005" (all flutes).

Causes	Remedies
Excessive pressure on feed rolls.	Adjust to proper pressure.
Worn feed rolls.	Replace as needed
Excessive pressure on pull rolls.	Re-set gap. Adjust pull rolls.
Worn pull rolls.	Replace as needed.

Manufacturer's Joint Too Wide

Refers to width of manufacturer's joint — in excess of specification limits.

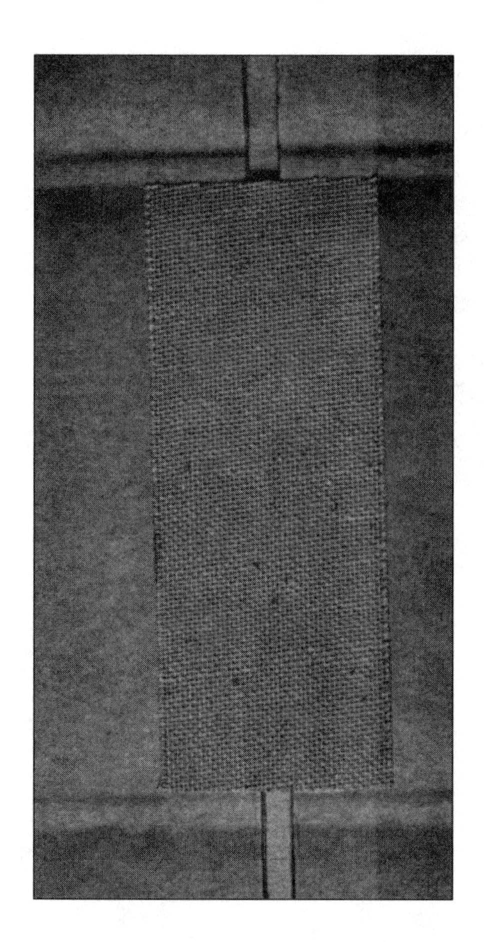

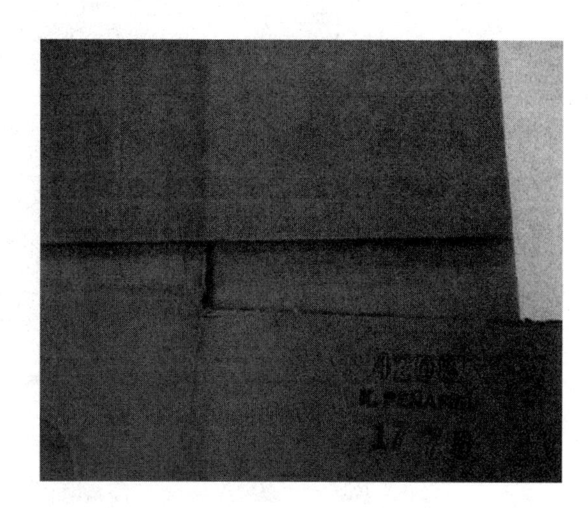

Causes

Scoring allowances incorrect.

Printer slitter operation or section set-up incorrect.

Excessive roll over in score line.

Short sheets from corrugator.

Blank not folding correctly.

Remedies

Check specifications for error.

Adjust scoring and trim knives set up on the press.

Adjust scoring pressure on press.

Check corrugator.

Adjust folding rails, belts, runs and/or swords.
For semi-automatic machines, operator can manipulate blank to achieve a proper width gap.

Manufacturer's Joint Too Narrow or Overlapped

Gap of less than 1/16 space or an actual overlap between first and fourth panels—not counting the tab area.

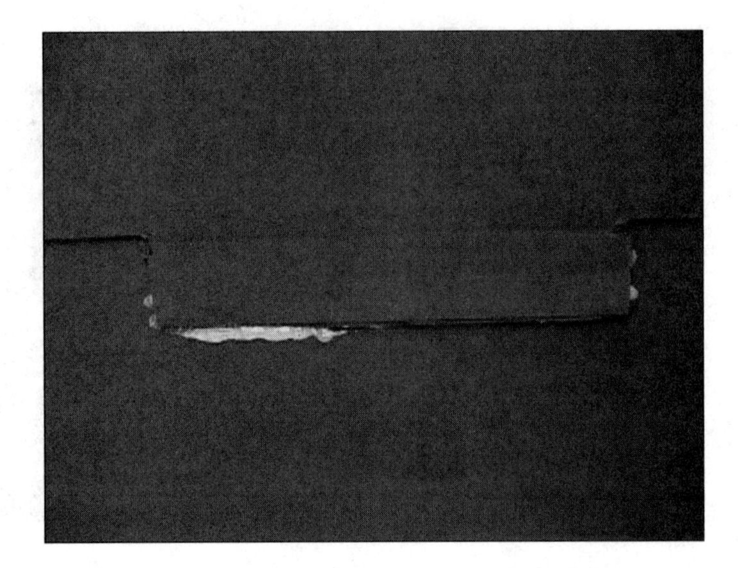

Causes	Remedies
Case not folding correctly.	Semi-automatic machine operation can manipulate case to get better fold. On semi-automatic stitches and tapers, printer-slotter operation or section must score deep enough without excessive pull roll or slotter head pressure to get good fold.
Improper machine adjustment.	Check to see if guides are too tight on automatic stitchers or tapers.
Scoring allowances incorrect.	Check specifications for error.
Press set-up incorrect.	Adjust trim knife set up.
Rolling scores.	Adjust scoring pressure. Adjust folding rails, belts, folding rods and/or swords.

Manufacturer's Joint Width Inconsistent

Inconsistent folding; inconsistent gap in manufacturer's joint.

No Photo Available

Causes	Remedies
Insufficient score pressure	Increase pressure.
Worn male or female scorers	Replace as necessary.
Improper score profile	Replace with proper configuration.
Scoring shafts out of parallel	Reparallel.
Loose side guide	Tighten to proper, fixed position.
Improperly positioned folding rails or rods	Reset to proper score/rail position.
Excessive slotting and score pressure	Back off pressure to proper nip.
Skewing of sheets before reaching folder	Check pull roll collar and pull band settings.

Manufacturer's Joint Skewed (Fishtailed) or out of square (Flap Scores don't line up within 1/8") or a Combination of the Two Conditions

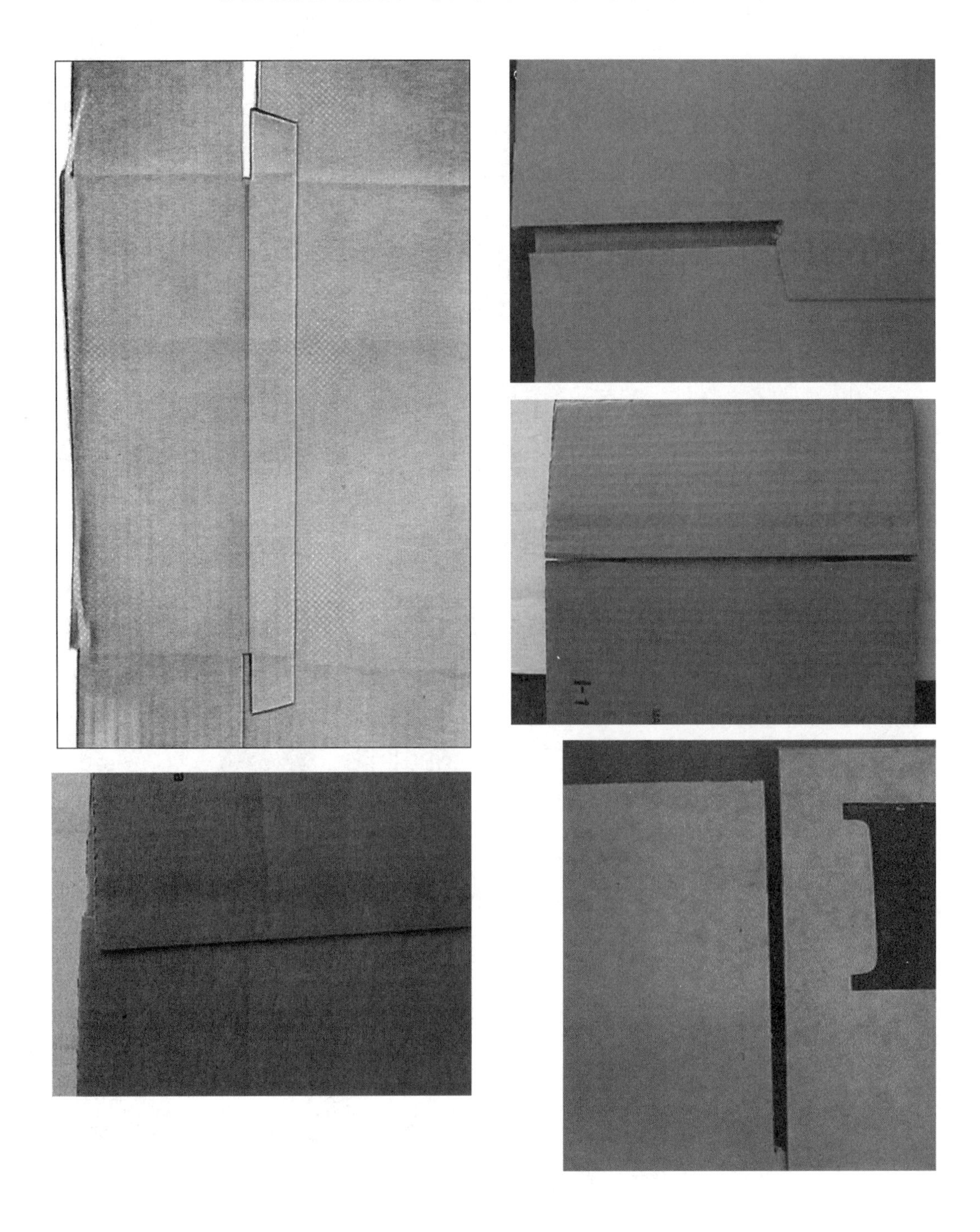

Manufacturer's Joint Skewed (Fishtailed) or out of square (Flap Scores don't link up within 1/8") or a Combination of the Two Conditions

(Continued)

Condition 1: Box blank becoming skewed with respect to the centerline of the Flexo folder gluer, a folder gluer, or a proceeding printer slotter operation.

Causes	Remedies
One or more nip points in the press and/or folding section mis-adjusted or out-of-parallel causing blank to become skewed.	Check and adjust the following as needed so box blank feeds evenly into the machine and travels through the machine without becoming skewed with respect to the machine center line: • Feed mechanism (kicker bar or lead edge feeder • Feed rolls • Printing cylinder/impression roll • Pull rolls/collars • Slotting and/or scoring shafts • Drag in the folding rails

Condition 2: Problems with or in folding section

Causes	Remedies
Upper or lower folding rails not properly positioned.	Check dimensions and adjust as necessary.
Carrying belts not equally tensioned	Adjust belt tensioning device and equalize both sides.
Improper folding motion	Adjust to more gradual, continuous fold.
Slot and crease alignment incorrect	Align score to center of slot.
Improper score	Set for proper scoring.
Worn belts	Replace as necessary.
Folding belts (top belts for a bottom printer — bottom belts for a top printer) speeds not consistent with each other or not having a slight over-speed relative to the companion belts on the matching folding rail.	Check with tachometer and adjust/correct synchronization. If available, use rheostat to adjust belt speeds.
Folding rails out of parallel	Reparallel folding rails.
Squaring device improperly set	Adjust for adequate squaring (spanking) action.

Improper Glue-Lap Tab (or Stitch Tab)

Refers to wide or narrow glue-lap.

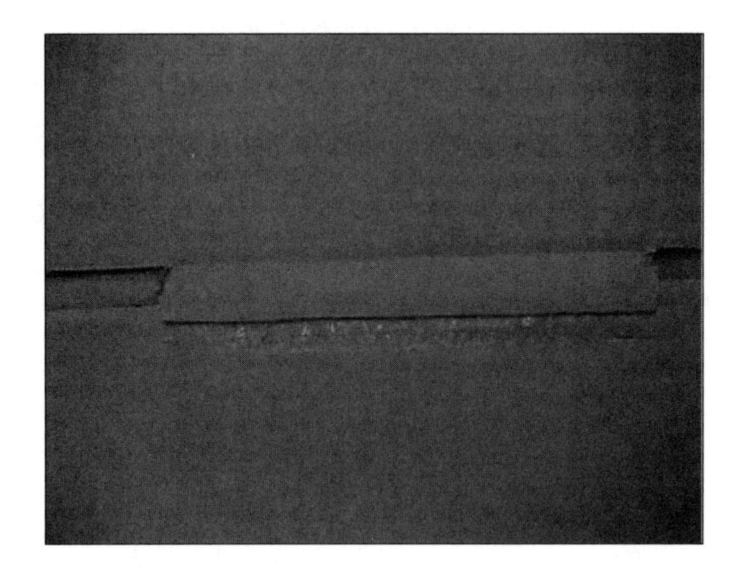

Causes

Glue-lap tab cut too wide or too narrow.

Blank too short.

Remedies

Adjust side guides in feed hopper so box blanks are fed in properly.
Adjust for proper knife settings.

Adjust scoring and trim knife set-up on the press section or operation, if possible; re-run order at corrugator if not.

D. Counter Ejection Section Problems

Problem	Causes	Remedies
Jamming at counter ejector	Loose liner	Remove defective blanks.
	Skewed blanks	Adjust pull roll collars.
	Sheet slippage	Worn belts–replace.
	Side guides and folding rails improperly set	Adjust clearance between upper and lower folding rails.
	Hold-down blower improperly positioned or inoperative	Reposition or repair.
	Improperly timed spanker	Retime.
Incorrect stacking	Too much pressure by compression bar or hold-down	Use minimum pressure from compression bar or hold-down.
	Boxes not hitting backstop	Speed up understacker and/or reset backstop.
Boxes are not being delivered from bottom of squaring hopper	Boxes glued together	Check glue applicator for drips.
		Check for short sheets.
		Check to see that glue laps are being completely cut and waste is being removed.
	Box hanging up on gates	Gates too tight; adjust.
	Boxes releasing from gates two a time or wedging at gates	Gates too loose; adjust.
	Boxes hang up in hopper	Backstop too tight; adjust.
Dragging blanks at pushoff	Pusher partially contacting the top blank of the subsequent pile	Readjust the pusher height.
Pusher operates erratically	Defective box counter	Replace counter.
	Dirt on electric eye	Remove dirt from electric eye.
Incorrect count	Pusher	Check pusher height and readjust if necessary.
	Hold-down height incorrect	Readjust hold-down height.
	Defective box counter	Replace counter.
	Dirt on electric eye	Remove dirt from electric eye.
	Links in chain mechanism removed (short counts) or added (long counts) on chain driven sweep arm bundle ejector machines	Chain must have exact number of links as specified by manufacturer.
Bundles not being delivered from ejector	Delivery belts not running	Turn on delivery belt drive.

E. Glue Lap Problems

Blocking of Finished Glue-Lap Boxes

Refers to adhesive that is squeezed out beyond the edges of the glue-lap resulting in sticking of containers in the bundles.

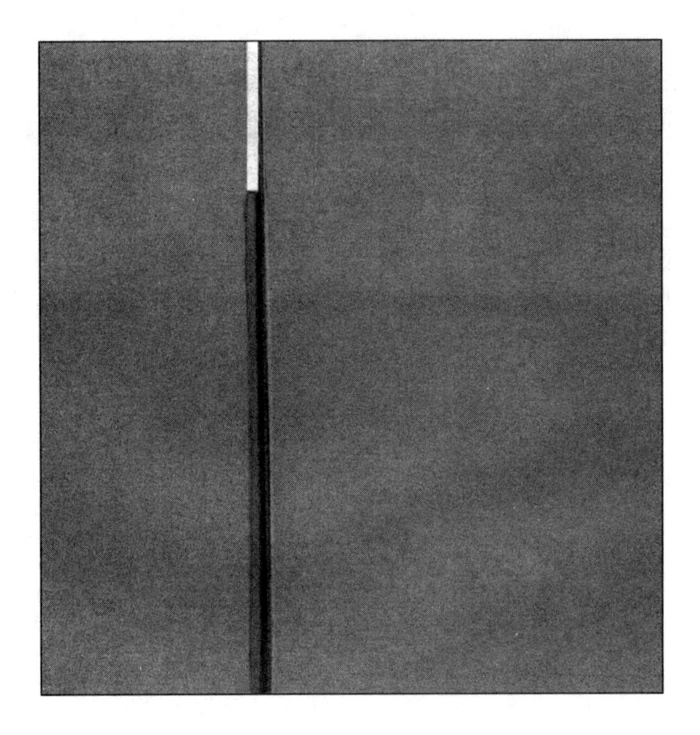

Causes	Remedies
Excessive pressure on conveyor belt.	Reduce pressure or conveyor belt.
Improper adhesive viscosity.	Correct for smooth flo and/or to machine manufacturer's recommendations.
Improper timing of glue roll or extrusion head.	Re-adjust glue roll or extrusion head. Adjust electronic activation mechanism controlling glue extrusion.
Improper placement of extrusion head.	Adjust set-up to properly locate extrusion application.
Extrusion head pattern too wide for width of glue tab.	Replace extrusion head with one of a proper size. Check glue tab width. If incorrect advise Scheduling to correct on future orders.
Too much flow from pump.	Reduce flow.
Too little clearance between applicator and pressure wheel (glue wheel applicators).	Adjust to proper gap.
Metering shoe not seated properly on wheel (give wheel applicators).	Remove any buildup of dried glue, scrap, or paper dust. Ensure maximum viscosity of manufacturer is not exceeded.
Return hose kinked.	Remove kink.

Internal Fiber Failure at Glue-Lap Joint

Refers to fiber separation of liner at glue-lap joint.

Causes	Remedies
Weak surface fiber bond.	Obtain liner with adequate surface fiber bond.
Insufficient glue.	Adjust adhesive application to a minimum 80% glue coverage.

Glue-Lap not Adhered to Board After Pressure Section

Refers to lack of adhesion of glue between lap and board after pressure has been applied at the glue-lap machine.

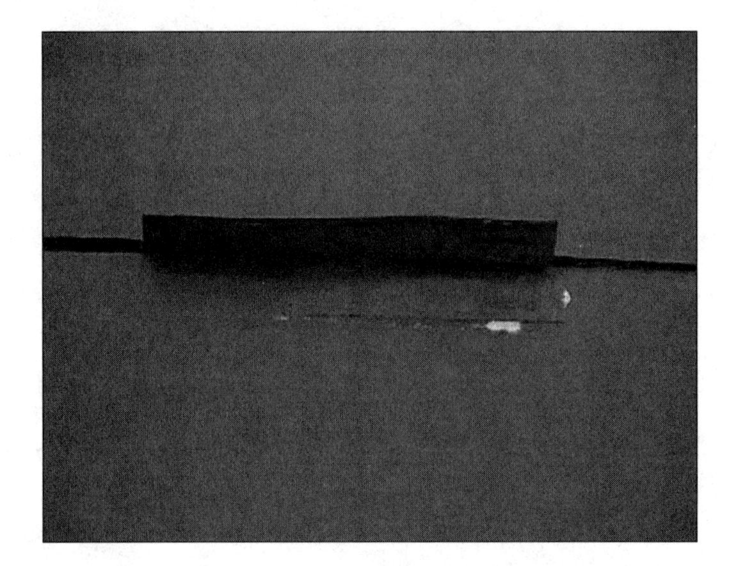

Causes	Remedies
Poor penetration of glue.	Adjust speed of machine. Apply wetting agent if practical, or change adhesive.
Insufficient glue.	Adjust adhesive applicator roll or extrusion unit.
Warped board.	Increase hold down pressure.
Insufficient compression time.	Increase compression time or obtain faster setting adhesive.
Improper compression action.	Make sure hold down mechanism in accumulating hopper is operating properly. Make sure compression mechanism for newly formed bundles of boxes is applying sufficient pressure. Make sure adhesive viscosity, pH, % solids meet machinery manufacturer's recommendations. Make sure shingling compression section (where used) is applying sufficient pressure.

Trim Adhered to Glue-Lap/Tab Knives Not Cutting

Refers to loose trim falling and adhering to joint. (May occur when blanks are trimmed and slotted on flexo folder gluers or on printing presses.)

Causes	Remedies
Tab trim removal system not effective	Adjust brush, air nozzle etc. for effectiveness. Add system to machine.
Dull tab knives or slotting knives.	Check: Replace slotting knives or tab knives as necessary.
Improperly set tab knife.	Adjust height of tab knife. Adjust lateral position of tab knife to achieve a proper cut.
Tab knife on steel to steel machines set too deep causing bouncing.	Adjust.
Use of improper tab knife.	Use proper tab knife for board flute.
Broken tab knife.	Replace.
Tab anvil worn.	Replace anvil cover.
Tab anvil not rotating freely.	Adjust or replace anvil.

Weak Glue-Lap Bond

Glue joint not adhered at all or fails with very little pressure.

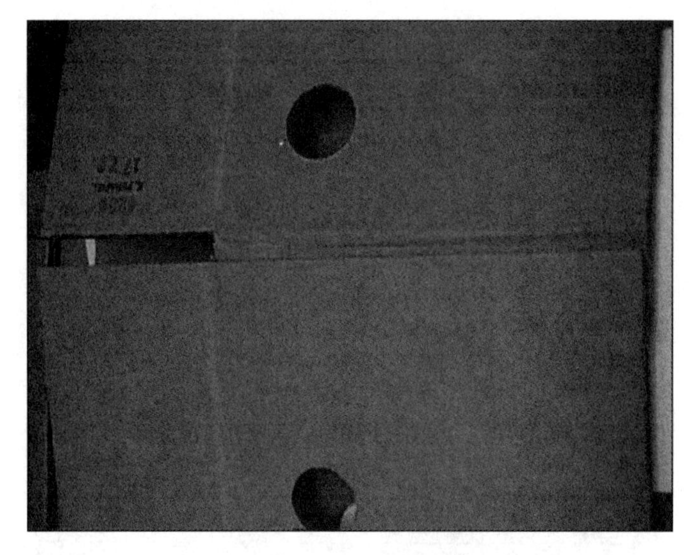

Causes	Remedies
Insufficient glue application.	Check sheet for glue pattern and enough glue in reservoir.
Poor glue penetration.	Check glue viscosity, tack and setup time.
Too short a compression time.	Either lengthen compression or slow machine down.
Glue setting up either too slow or fast.	Change adhesive.
Extrusion system not working properly.	See pages on extrusion-type glue application systems (pages 195 and 196).
Glue dries on application surface.	Remove boxes in folding section following stoppages. Use adhesive with sufficient open time.
Glue dries on both surfaces.	Check to see if hold down mechanism in accumulating section is exerting sufficient pressure. Open time of adhesive too long. Use adhesive with a shorter open time.
Distortion of box in squaring section.	Adjust front stop on squaring section so that distortion doesn't occur but squaring is accomplished.
Insufficient flow of glue.	Increase flow from pump. Repair or replace as necessary. Check hoses for restrictions and correct as necessary.
Contaminated glue mechanism.	Clean as required.
Viscosity too high.	Check viscosity against manufacturer's recommendation.
Excessive clearance between applicator and pressure wheel (wheel-type applicators).	Adjust to proper gap.

Extruded Glue Mechanism Problems

Problem	Causes	Remedies
No glue	No power to control	Turn on circuit breaker; turn on glue unit. Find source of short circuit.
	Blown fuse; tripped circuit breaker	Replace fuse; reset breaker.
	Defective pump	Repair or replace pump.
	Clogged filter	Clean filter.
	Clogged glue supply line	Clean line.
	No air pressure	Turn on air to recommended pressure.
	Low air pressure	Adjust to correct pressure.
	Low level or no glue	Add glue.
	Flow rate too low	Adjust for more glue.
Insufficient glue	Viscosity too high	Replace with proper viscosity glue.
	Glue too cold	Add warm glue or replace glue supply.
	Low glue supply	Add glue.
	Leak in air system	Find and correct.
	Obstruction in glue or air supply line	Clean lines.
	Clogged filter	Clean filter.
	Obstruction in glue applicator head	Remove and clean in warm water or a recommended solvent.
	Flow rate too low	Adjust for more glue.
Excessive glue	Flow rate too high	Adjust for less glue.
	Viscosity too low	Replace with proper viscosity glue.
	Air pressure too high	Adjust air pressure setting.
Erratic glue pattern	Air in glue lines	Bleed or purge.
	Pulse generator	Check tension of drive belt and functioning of pulse generator.
	Clogged glue applicator	Clean in warm water.
	Obstruction in glue supply lines	Clean and flush lines.
	Air pressure too high or low	Adjust to proper setting.
	Clogged glue filters	Clean filters.
	Dirty sensor light	Clean.
	Applicator pressure to sheet not correct	Adjust.
	Worn glue applicator	Replace.

Extruded Glue Mechanism Problems

(Continued)

Problem	Causes	Remedies
Glue beads on lead and trail edge of sheet	Air in glue system	Bleed or purge system.
	Defective electric solenoid	Replace.
	Dirty or damaged glue valve	Clean, rebuild or replace glue valve.
	Worn glue applicator	Replace.
Glue pattern trails	Air in glue system	Bleed or purge glue system.
	Defective electric solenoid	Replace.
	Worn glue applicator	Replace.
	Clogged exhaust port on electric air valve	Replace or clean.
	Improper contact of board surface to glue head	Adjust glue head for proper height and angle. Adjust support under head for proper tension and support.
Glue pattern starting too early	Wrong input information	Check against specification sheet.
	Control problem	Adjust turn on delay potentiometer.
Glue pattern starting too late	Control problem	Adjust turn on delay potentiometer.
	Photo sensor	Check for contamination or mounting problems.
Scrap causing intermittent improper gluing	Scrap	Refer to "Trim Adhered … " page 193 in this section of the manual.

Improper Folding At Glue Tab

Refers to the board readily breaking at the glue-lap rather than at the lap score line.

Causes	Remedies
Insufficient score on glue lap.	Increase score depth at press or pre-break lap score.
Insufficient glue coverage.	Adjust glue applicator.
Improper crushing using crushing collars (where available).	Set crushing collars properly.

F. Stitching Problems

Stitches—Broken or Malformed (Unclinched)

Stitches that do not add to strength of containers and detract from its visual appearance.

Staple	Trouble	Causes	Remedies
a.	Perfect staple.		
b.	Right leg short.	Wire spool dragging.	Adjust wire spool tension.
		Wire slipping in wire feed gears.	Check tension setting of wire feed gears.
		Upper and/or lower wire tube clogged or worn.	Check wire feed tubes.
		Cutter block not properly positioned with relation to gripper.	Make adjustments.
		Improper wire feed due to over lubricated or worn wire feed clutch.	Check operation of wire feed clutch.
		Wire slipping in gripper due to normal wear of gripper bar clamp piece or insufficient tension in clamp piece spring.	Check gripper bar clamp piece and spring.
c.	Left leg short.	Cutter block not properly positioned with relation to gripper.	Adjust length of left leg.
d.	Staple corner buckled.	Chipped or broken driver.	Check driver ends for signs of damage; reverse or replace driver.
e.	Either or both legs buckled.	Wrong size wire being used for work being stitched.	Check wire size for work being stitched.
		Dull wire cutters.	Check movable end stationary cutters; sharpen or replace cutters.
		Worn supporter, or supporter retracts too easily due to insufficient spring tension	Check for worn supporter and broken or weak supporter spring.

Stitches—Broken or Malformed (Unclinched)

Stitches that do not add to strength of containers and detract from its visual appearance.

(Continued)

Staple	Trouble	Causes	Remedies
f.	Bent crown.	Wrong size wire being used for work being stitched.	Check wire size for work being stitched.
		Supporter retracts too easily.	Check for weak supporter spring.
		Wrong setting of stitcher adjustment for thickness of work being stitched.	Check stitcher adjustment for thickness of work being stitched.
g.	Left leg missing.	Wire slipping in gripper due to normal wear of gripper bar clamp piece or clamp piece spring.	Check gripper bar clamp piece and clamp piece spring.
		Gripper out of alignment with formers.	Check to see that formers and gripper are in proper alignment.
		Obstruction in feed channel.	Clean out feed channel.
h.	Right leg missing.	Wire slipping in wire feed gears.	Check tension setting of wire feed gears; check for worn gears.
		Refer to causes for "Left leg missing" (above).	Refer to remedies for "Left leg missing" (above).
		Gripper not operating properly due to broken or weak gripper bar holding springs.	Check for broken or weak gripper spring.
i.	Staple comes out in pieces.	See causes for "Left" and "Right leg missing"(above).	Refer to remedies for "Left" and "Right leg missing" (above).
		Supporter edges worn sharp.	Check for worn supporter.
		Former grooves clogged up.	Lubricate wire at wire tube.
		Wire too large.	Check wire being used.
j.	Corner of staple broken or nearly broken through.	Wire too large.	Check wire being used.
		Supporter edges worn sharp.	Check for worn supporter.
		Driver corners too sharp; or worn formers.	Check for worn formers and driver.
k.	Corner of staple rounded.	Worn anvil surface of gripper bar.	Check for worn gripper bar.

Stitches—Poor Clinching

Stitches that snag on straight edge as it slides over stitch.

Staple	Trouble	Causes	Remedies
a.	Perfect stitch (.175 to .500 in. crown width)		
b.	Perfect stitch (crown widths greater than .500 in.)		
c.	Loose Clinch.	Wrong setting of stitcher ad-adjustment for thickness of work; clinchers set too low.	Check setting of stitcher for thickness of work being stitched, and raise clinchers.
d.	Legs spread.	Worn wire cutters.	Check movable and stationary cutters; sharpen or replace cutters.
		Former grooves worn.	Check formers; replace if grooves are worn.
		Wire straightener not properly adjusted.	Check setting of wire straight-ener.
		Thickness or work beyond capacity of machine.	Check thickness capacity of stitcher.
e.	Staple legs contracted.	Worn wire cutters.	Check movable and stationary cutters; sharpen or replace.
		Wire straightener not properly adjusted	Check setting of wire straightener.
f.	Crown buckled, tearing work.	Wrong setting of machine adjustment for thickness of work.	Check setting of stitcher for thickness of work being stitched.
g.	Only one leg clinched in.	Clinch not in alignment with driver.	Align clincher and driver.
		Dull cutter.	Replace cutter.
h.	Short legs.	Insufficient wire draw.	Increase amount of wire draw.
i.	Legs cross.	Wire draw too great.	Decrease amount of wire draw.
j.	Uneven clinching.	Clincher not level and parallel with formers.	Adjust clincher setting.

Stitches—Incorrect Number

Number of stitches at manufacturer's joint less than or greater than number specified.

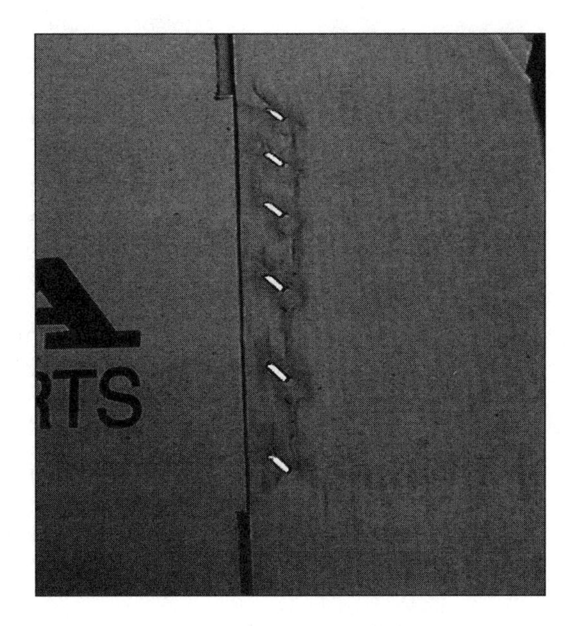

Causes	Remedies
Incorrect setup.	Check dial setting.
Incorrect tension drum spring.	Correct drum spring tension.
Incorrect setting of screw that contacts dial control.	Adjust screw.
Incorrect brake adjustment.	Adjust brake.
Trip gauge laying too heavy on case.	Adjust springs to raise trip gauge.
Clutch repeating.	Broken clutch pawl.

Stitches—Improper Spacing

Stitches not equally spaced along stitch tab - tie stitch is an exception.

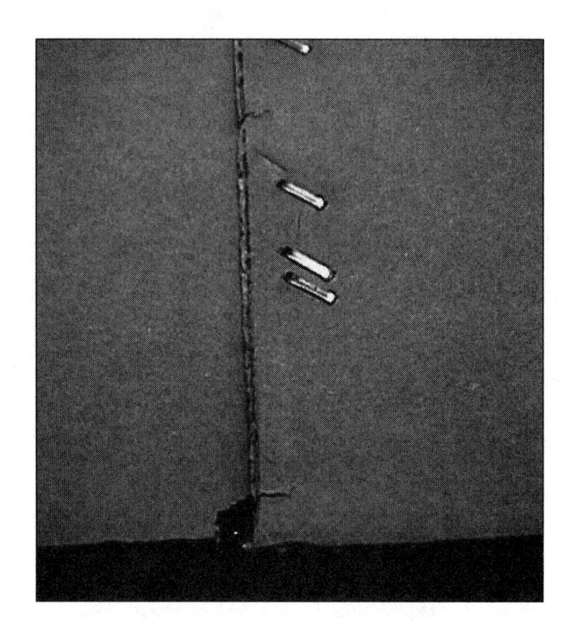

Causes	Remedies
Lower feed rollers not tight.	Tighten rollers.
Insufficient pressure of feed rollers.	Increase pressure of rollers on box.
Brakes controlling overthrow of feed clutch not setting properly.	Reset brake.
Trip gauge not lifting up enough to clear box.	Adjust springs so trip gauge lifts properly.
Worn teeth or improper engagement of step feed with clutch.	Replace or clean clutch.
Box feed roller ratchet clutch worn or dirty.	Replace or clean ratchet.
Oil on feed rollers.	Clean feed rollers.
Side gauges set too tight.	Adjust side gauges.

Stitches—Poor Vertical Placement

Any stitch having one or both legs clinching off the stitch tab or the end stitch is more than 1-1/8 in. from the flap score line.

Causes	Remedies
Trip gauge plate not dropping soon enough.	Adjust spring to cause trip gauge plate to drop faster.
Boxes being fed too fast.	Slow down feeding of boxes.
Trip gauge plate not properly adjusted.	Re-adjust trip gauge plate.
Side gauges set incorrectly.	Re-adjust side gauge position.

Stitches—Poor Lateral Placement

Stitches that are away from center of stich tab so that one or both legs of stitch do not clinch tab to box panel.

Causes	Remedies
Side gauges set incorrectly.	Side gauges should be reset to locate stitch tab in proper relation to stitcher head.
Poor fold of cases.	Operator may have to manipulate case to get better fold. Make sure printer-slotter is scoring case deep enough to get good fold. Also check to see that slotter head pressure is not excessive.

Stitch Lap—Poor Folding

Stich lap breaking at stitches rather than lap score line.

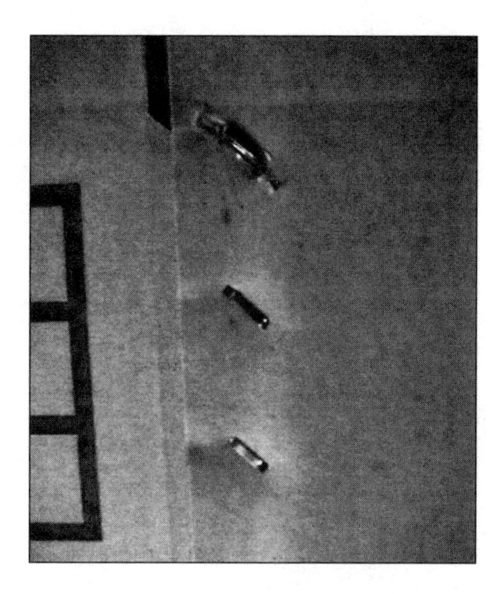

Causes	Remedies
Insufficient score of stitch lap.	Printer must score deep enough. Prebreak score at printer-slotter.
Stitch placement.	Place stitches laterally as near score as possible.
Excessivc pressure on stitches.	Adjust stitch formers to crush into board as little as possible.

G. Taping Problems

Tape—Cut Crooked

Refers to tape being out of parallel, either top to bottom or side to side.

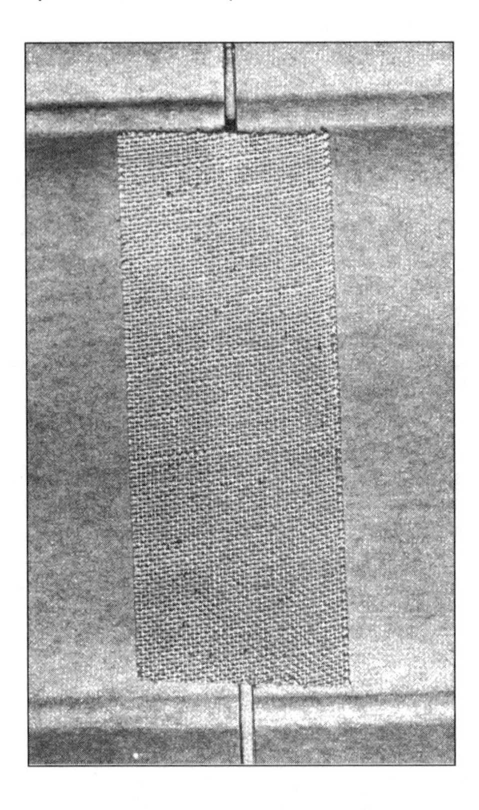

Causes	Remedies
Cut-off knife out of parallel.	Align knife perpendicular to tape.
Tape guides out of adjustment.	Adjust tape guides.
Cut-off knives dull.	Replace or sharpen knives.

Tape—Long or Short

Refers to variations of tape length causing tape to extend beyond or fall short of flap scoreline.

Causes	Remedies
Machine set up incorrectly.	Check for correct setting and adjust.
Dirty or worn out contact points.	Clean or replace.
Slipping of conveyor belt or feed roll.	Adjust pressure.
Slipping of ratchet.	Adjust or repair.
Tape not tensioned properly.	Adjust tension of tape feed roll.

Tape—Not Centered

Refers to uniformity of tape application to both panels of manufacturer's joint.

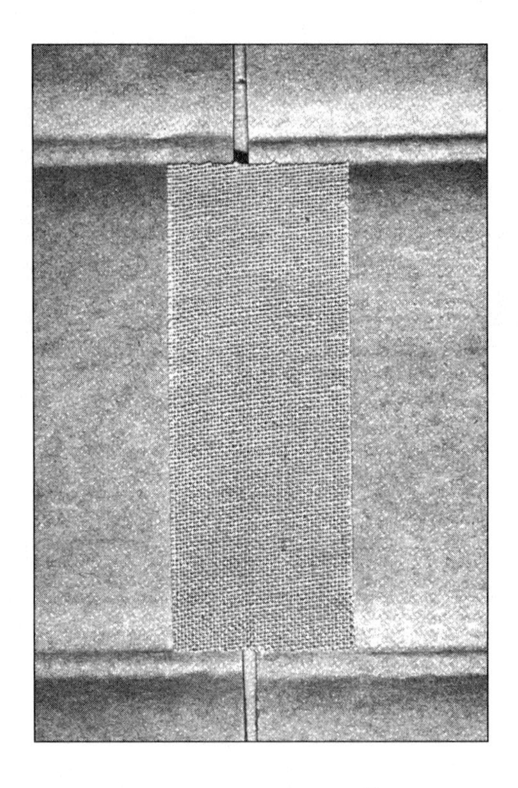

Causes	Remedies
Spring tension out of adjustment.	Adjust tension.
Side guides not centered.	Adjust alignment guides to center tape.
Machine not timed properly.	Check timing mechanism and correct.
Switches not operating properly.	Clean and repair switches.
Feed gauge not centering box.	Adjust feed gauge.

H. Common Curtain Coating Problems

Problem	Causes	Remedies
Pinholes	(1) Elongated holes caused by bubbles in the melt due to air entrainment from splashing, enfolding, pump leaks, etc.	(1) Raise wax temperature; eliminate splashing, enfolding, pump leaks (Do not use anti-foaming additives).
	(2) Round holes forming after laydown from moist board or dense spots due to sizing, calendering, coating or printing.	(2) Ensure board not wet and porosity uniform. Use permeable inks or coatings.
	(3) High wax temperature causing excessive penetration.	(3) Lower wax temperature.
	(4) Insufficient coating laydown.	(4) Increase wax load.
	(5) Uncoated fibers acting as wicks.	(5) Use smoother paper or more wax.
Poor adherence	(1) Low wax temperature causing insufficient penetration for good mechanical "grab."	(1) Raise wax temperature.
	(2) High-density board limiting wax penetration.	(2) Raise wax temperature; use higher porosity board.
Scoreline cracking or staining	(1) Insufficient coating adherence allowing lifting of the coating away from the board surface when score is flexed.	(1) Increase adherence by increasing wax temperature.
	(2) Coating "bridging" score.	(2) Raise coating head and/or change angle of blanks going through curtain. Increase head pressure if possible.
	(3) Coating not sufficiently flexible for intended use.	(3) Use coating designed for higher degree of flexibility.
	(4) Flex rate too fast during box set-up.	(4) Decrease box forming machine speed; external folding shoes to decrease angular folding rate.
Uneven wax load across board (stripe effect in falling curtain or laydown)	(1) Dirty or improperly adjusted orifice.	(1) Clean and/or adjust orifice.
	(2) Incompatible wax mixture being used.	(2) Replace wax in system.
Darkened coating	(1) Oxidation of wax due to excessively high temperature.	(1) Reduce coating temperature. Reduce time and temperature of pre-melting. Reduce recirculation time.

H. Common Curtain Coating Problems

(Continued)

Problem	Causes	Remedies
Poor gloss	(1) High wax load.	(1) Decrease wax load to reasonable level (7-8 lbs/Msf.)
	(2) High ambient temperature.	(2) Reduce ambient temperature or cool laydown more quickly with air circulation over coated surface.
	(3) Development of surface "dust" or "bloom" after coating due to migration of wax out of blend.	(3) Avoid wide temperature contrasts between coating and contact surfaces. Use alternate coating blend.
Shadowing	(1) Bent, creased or severely warped board.	(1) Use flatter board or provide hold-down until board gets through curtain.
Coating breaks—unstable curtain	(1) Wax temperature too high.	(1) Lower temperature (if below cloud point, raise temperature).
	(2) Dirty orifice; dirt or bubbles in curtain.	(2) Clean orifice; correct for bubbles (see above).
	(3) Incompatible and/or badly oxidized wax in system.	(3) Replace wax in system.
	(4) Drafts or mechanical vibration reaching coating head area.	(4) Eliminate drafts or vibration.
	(5) Warped board "springing" from in-feed nip roll.	(5) Provide hold-down until board is through the curtain.
	(6) "Pops" or "fisheyes" caused by silicones or other surfactant contaminants.	(6) Check for airborne contaminants, particularly from printing operations.
Blocking	(1) Wax melting point too low for end-use application.	(1) Use higher melting point wax formulation.
	(2) Coated surfaces too hot when stacked.	(2) Direct cool air stream over surface before stacker; increase time (distance) between curtain and stacker.